WITNEY SCROTUM

A Touch of Daniel
I Didn't Know You Cared
Except You're a Bird
Call it A Canary
Mog
The Stirk of Stirk
Shemerelda
The Home Front
Tales From a Long Room
More Tales From a Long Room
The Brigadier Down Under
The Brigadier in Season
The Brigadier's Tour
The Brigadier's Brief Lives
Tales from Witney Scrotum
Uncle Mort's North Country
Uncle Mort's South Country
Hayballs
Winston

PETER TINNISWOOD

WITNEY SCROTUM

HUTCHINSON
LONDON

The right of Peter Tinniswood to be
identified as Author of this work has been asserted
by Peter Tinniswood in accordance with the
Copyright, Designs and Patents Act, 1988

1 3 5 7 9 8 6 4 2

This edition first published in 1995 by
Hutchinson

Random House Group Ltd
20 Vauxhall Bridge Road, London SW1V 2SA

Random House Australia (Pty) Ltd
20 Alfred Street, Milsons Point, Sydney, NSW 2061, Australia

Random House New Zealand Ltd
PO Box 40–086, Glenfield, Auckland 10, New Zealand

Random House South Africa (Pty) Ltd
PO Box 337, Bergvlei, 2012, South Africa

ISBN 0 09 174460 1

A CiP catalogue record for this
book is available from the British Library

Paper used by Random House UK Ltd are natural recyclable
products made from wood grown in sustainable forests. The
manufacturing processes conform to the environmental
regulations of the country of origin

Typeset by Pure Tech Corporation,
Pondicherry, India

Printed and bound in Great Britain by
Mackays of Chatham PLC, Kent

CONTENTS

*Dedicated to Mr Ken Cranston and
Lancashire County Cricket Club*

CHAPTER ONE

The Commodore

Times change.

My God, how they change.

What tricks they play. What perfidies they inflict upon us. How they cackle and how they snicker at our minor joys and our trivial woes.

Once I was a little boy.

Nanny smelled of unrequited ink and looked the spitting image of Field Marshal von Ludendorff.

Cook ran off with an Armenian bassoonist and fifteen oven gloves.

Every Friday evening, when he was home from manoeuvres, my father of late and loathsome memory would, without the slightest reason, thrash me soundly about the buttocks with his hickory-shafted niblick.

Mother collected antique Belgian umbrella stands.

Once I was a young man.

I had ambitions.

I wanted to open the batting and open the bowling for Glamorgan, play outside right for Preston North End and win the Cheltenham Gold Cup on a horse.

I wanted to teach the rudiments of leg spin and late outswing to bold and wicked ladies from the musical theatre in the West End of London and drink cream soda from Percy Fender's submariner's slippers.

I wanted to climb Everest, swim the Hellespont and drive a one-man trolley bus in Burton-on-Trent.

Once I was a young, married man.

Oh, the ambitions I had then.

I wanted to be a single, married man.

Time passed.

Mr Raymond Illingworth was born in a humble manger to the rear of the Pudsey Non-Political tram clinic.

Scientists discovered the medicated arch support.

The world was convulsed by violent upheavals which irrevocably changed the whole fabric of society.

Wars, revolutions, droughts, famine and plague toppled great empires, destroyed ancient dynasties and decimated to perdition the manufacturers of stovepipe hats and ornamental colanders.

Worst of all, the LBW laws became completely incomprehensible to all but Sir Geoffrey Boycott and the terminally insane.

And now?

Now I live here in Witney Scrotum with the Lady Wife and her piggy little eyes, her squeaking golf shoes and her distinctive stuttering run-up to the fridge.

We cower behind the barricades of nostalgia, desperately trying to keep at bay the modern world with its greed, its brutality and its obdurate refusal to grant Test Match status to Holland.

How I hate the mores of contemporary society.

Well, not entirely, if the truth be known.

There is one aspect of modern life which I confess I applaud wholeheartedly.

It is this – its unrestrained prurience and nosiness, the desire to poke its beak into other people's busines, exposing to public scrutiny scandal, calumny, disgrace and abomination.

There was a time when I didn't give a fig to know that Sir Robert Boothby was having affairs concurrently and at the same time with Lady Dorothy Macmillan, Al Capone, Sir Stafford Cripps, Nobby Stiles, E. Eynon Evans and the entire company of Doctor Crock and his Crackpots.

What did I care that Brian Statham was 'a duffer' with puff pastry?

What possible business of mine was it to learn that the Chief of the Defence Staff had been seen dancing the rhumba with Mr David Mellor at The Bienvenida Country Club, Lambton-on-Yeo?

But time has passed over the surface of my mind, leaving behind its sinuous, slug-like, slimy trails and changed forever my attitude to life.

More.

I want more scandal.

Give me more prating and prattling.

More, more, more, I say.

Twinkle twinkle little Star.

The Sun also rises.

I cannot get enough titbits of gossip from the gentlemen's mixed sauna at Lord's and dollops of tittle-tattle from the girls in the typing pool at Wisden Cricketers' Almanack.

So that's what Miss Judith Chalmers gets up to with Mr Neil Durden-Smith's hyphen?

How could Chris Lewis possibly give of his best for his country when he habitually wears Miss Joanna Lumley's teeth?

And thus it is that I broach the subject of my good friend and neighbour, the Commodore.

Over the years I have been constantly pestered and badgered by countless scores of readers, pleading with me, nay, demanding of me to give details of the life and times of my beloved nautical comrade in snorters and snifters.

Where was he born?

Where did he serve?

What was his taste in agricultural machinery?

What were his opinions regarding the culling of typewriter mechanics?

Enough, dear readers, enough.

I am now prepared to reveal all.

No prevarications.

No 'shoving the dirt under the carpet'.

No pleading giddiness and a sicky headache and hiding myself behind the nuptial bolster.

Here for your delectation is the true and fully authenticated 'historie' of the Commodore.

He was born of mixed parentage (man and woman) on a houseboat moored somewhat haphazardly on the Peak Forest canal thus giving him residential qualifications to play cricket for Derbyshire and ice hockey for The British Inland Waterways Board.

His father came from a long and distinguished line of itinerant bus stop designers and at the time of his only son's birth was employed in a temporary capacity as chief wallaby catcher to the Chapel-en-le-Frith Rural District Council.

His mother was a lady of some considerable refinement and gentility, who had once been presented at court to Queen Alexandra, who had sent her back to her parents with a label attached to her neck bearing the inscription 'Not Known At This Address'.

With such richly distinctive blood coursing through his veins it was only natural that the Commodore should aim for the very highest pinnacles of achievement in life.

And thus it was that he applied for a position as junior salesman in the soft furnishings department of his local branch of the Co-operative Wholesale Society.

Alas, it was not to be.

He failed his entrance examinations dismally, doing particularly badly in the viva on loose covers.

It was here at the lowest point in his young life that Lady Luck stepped in.

During a Saturday night's wild carousing behind the whippet stadium at Matlock Bath he had the great good fortune to be press-ganged by a detachment of armed Sea Scouts and sent in irons to the Royal Naval Academy at Dartmouth.

To his astonishment he settled in immediately and proved himself to be an able and willing scholar.

In his first year he came top in anchor recognition, second in sea sickness and joint fifth in sticking coloured flags into maps of a vaguely nautical nature.

By the time he had graduated he had learned all the intricacies of sewing toggles on duffel coats, invisibly mending the lapels on waterproof life jackets and was 'second to none' in swallowing the sword of honour in a Force Nine gale.

Thus began a long and pre-eminent naval career of ramming, collisions, navigational errors, arson, mutiny and abandoning ship in harbour.

Among the important posts he held were commander of the armed sloop, HMS *Vertigo*, which assisted in the evacuation of Grange-over-Sands, third naval attaché to the Manchester Ship Canal Company at Eccles and chief navigator to the Royal Navy dry docks at Wolverhampton.

He served with equal eminence abroad.

He was thrice captured by pirates in the South China Sea, being ransomed on each occasion for three pantechnicons of Palethorpe's pork sausages and two packets of Capstan full strength cigarettes.

He was stricken by porthole poisoning in the Red Sea, laid low by a rash on his binnacle in the Bosphorus and washed overboard three times while serving on an inflatable minesweeper on Lake Titicaca.

It was a full life and a joyous life, and he lived it to the full.

He prospered particularly well on the social side, where his prowess in impersonating the royal yacht and juggling unexploded gash buckets on the poop decks of redundant battleships made him a firm favourite from the humblest stokers' mess to the highest Admiral's state cabin.

But like many an old salt it was the girls of the opposite gender who took his fancy and dominated his life.

And he stinted himself not in the wholehearted pursuance of their charms and their wiles and their easy winsome graces.

And so 'within next to no time' he became the favoured partner of Lord Mountbatten in Inter Fleet novelty Hokey Cokey competitions.

When Winston Churchill was First Lord of the Admiralty, he taught his wife and lovely daughters to spit tobacco juice like lascar sick-berth attendants and curse in Creole like defrocked ship's chaplains.

He was also rumoured to have been on 'more than intimate terms' with the naval correspondent of the *Daily Telegraph*, a gloomy man much given to writing rude words on the funnels of Home Fleet armed merchantmen.

But sadly it could not last.

As the great E.R. 'Elizabeth Regina' Dexter put it so elegantly and so exquisitely, 'all good things have to come to an end'.

In the early Thirties the Commodore was compelled to leave the Royal Navy, cashiered in considerable disgrace when he was discovered sleeping drunk and naked with the Prince of Wales, Virginia Woolf and a bent cake fork in the conning tower of HMS *Repulse*.

Their Lordships of the Admiralty stated in a reserved judgement that it was the damage to the cake fork which had finally swung the case against him.

And so what was he to do?

He was penniless.

He had no other trade or craft but an ability to tie simple knots and to shave under his armpits in cold water.

Fortunately for him these were precisely the qualities being avidly sought in new recruits for the fledgling BBC – as indeed they still are to this very day.

The wallahs at broadcasting HQ snapped him up of an instant and appointed him forthwith as chief sports commentator, the first in a celebrated line of virtuosos of the sporting ether, including H. Seton Fearneyhough with his inspiring commentaries on falconry and dental hygiene, Jasmine Rutter, mistress of rambling and internal operations, and Raymond Hoof, the doyen of ballooning.

It is not for me to chronicle the endless list of his triumphs.

These are too well documented in the annals of the BBC, tattooed on the inside legs of young maidens from the Radio Five rolling community arsonists' unit.

However, I do have in my possession a rare and extremely precious recording smuggled to me several years ago by a mole in the BBC archives department who exchanged it gratefully for a bag of sharks' teeth and an Anglo-Swedish pocket dictionary.

And this I propose to present to you in transcript form – most kindly done for me by dear Miss Roebuck from the dog biscuit shop on her mobile John Bull printing set.

So here goes:

INTERVIEWER:
My special studio guest today is undoubtedly the master non-pareil of radio commentary.
Commodore Froggatt.
Welcome, Commodore.
COMMODORE:
Beg your pardon?
INTERVIEWER:
I said , Welcome.
COMMODORE:
Thank you.
What did you say your name was?
INTERVIEWER:
Lynam.
Desmond Lynam.
COMMODORE:
Jolly good.
I'll remember that – given time.

By the way what's this lollipop thing sticking up in front of my face?

INTERVIEWER:

It's a microphone.

COMMODORE:

What?

INTERVIEWER:

It's the microphone.

It's for speaking into.

So you can be heard.

COMMODORE:

Jolly good.

I'll remember that – given time.

INTERVIEWER:

I'd like to ask you a few questions about your great days as a commentator on the radio.

I wonder – what do you remember about your first memorable broadcast as a commentator?

COMMODORE:

Nothing at all, old boy.

I do remember my second broadcast, though.

They sent me to the Oval to commentate on the Henley Regatta.

Well, when we got there, there were no rowing boats and, most crucial of all as far as I was concerned, not a trace of water.

So I turned to the chappie who seemed to be in charge and said:

'I don't know if it's occurred to you, old boy, but unless it rains pretty damn soon you don't stand a dog's chance of getting through the preliminary heats of the Diamond Sculls.'

Well, the poor booby looked absolutely astonished and his revolting Adam's apple started to bob up and down and he said in terms of utter confidence to me – and they did him great credit, I must say – he said that it was not in fact a regatta they were holding but rather a Test Match, England versus the West Indies.

So I thought to myself:

Well, I've nothing better to do.

I might as well commentate on that.

INTERVIEWER:

And, in fact, we do have a recording of that commentary. Perhaps you'd care to listen to it now?

COMMODORE:

Certainly.

What did you say your name was?

INTERVIEWER:

Lynam.

COMMODORE:

Jolly good.

I'll remember that – given time.

No.

On second thoughts I don't think I'll bother.

INTERVIEWER:

That's just what David Coleman always says to me.

Here we are then – the commentary.

(*We hear the sound of a rasping, scratching ancient commentary delivered by the Commodore many years ago.*)

COMMODORE:

Well here we are at Lords and . . .

What?

All right, then.

All right.

Here we are at the Oval.

I can't for the life of me think what difference it makes.

They're both equally damnable to me with their tepid beer and the ghastly smell of fly paper and the bare seats which are playing havoc with my piles and . . .

Never mind.

Not to bother about my troubles.

Let's get on with the game.

Well, it's England versus the West Indies and the news is that the darkies have won the toss, and elected to bat.

The England team is on the field now, and I'm damned if I can tell them apart.

They all look the same to me – shiftless, scrofulous and totally untrustworthy.

Anyway, the two West Indian openers have come out and they're very easy to tell apart.

One's small.

And the other is slightly taller.

And it looks as though the small one is about to take first strike.

And now the English opening bowler, a gangling lout who looks as though he's spilled half his breakfast down his flannels, is going back to his mark and . . .

Someone's standing in front of me.

I can't see a thing.

Sit down.

Sit down, I say.

Sit down, you scum.

He won't.

The bastard absolutely refuses.

Well, sod this for a lark – I'm going home.

(*End of recording*)

Perfection.

Bliss and enchantment.

I must say, dear readers, that when I heard that, a whole new world was opened up to me.

Never for an instant had I suspected that employees of the BBC ever went home.

I thought they stayed at Broadcasting House until they were overtaken by death.

And then, of course, they were appointed readers of the Ten O'Clock News.

CHAPTER TWO

Mentioned In Dispatches

For some reason quite unknown to me I seem to have achieved a certain eminence of fame.

Why?

I am aware that I hold 'a certain status' here in Witney Scrotum.

My rhubarb is of a consistently high standard and there is nothing to match the size and the ferocity of the earwigs in the Lady Wife's chrysanthemums.

Beyond the confines of the village I have also attained a modicum of notoriety.

I have twice been voted 'Personality of the Year' by the lady traffic wardens of both sexes in Keating New Town.

And on my last visit to London through the agency of moving train I had the great honour to be invited to spend the entire journey in the guard's van in the company of three insomniac Old English sheepdogs, five boxes of day-old pullets and a drunken free-fall parachutist from Weston-super-Mare.

But how to explain the recent flood of requests for my services?

Only last week I opened the Reg Harris Memorial Puncture Outfit extension to the mobile bicycle repair shop.

On Sunday I was principal speaker at an indoor garden fête in honour of the Friends of Sir Geoffrey Boycott Fund.

We collected 3s. 7d. in old money for the poor poverty-stricken creature and Mr Raymond Illingworth most graciously donated his personal voucher for a year's free supply of meals-on-wheels.

I am also currently involved in writing a foreword for a new collection of the early pensées of Nat Lofthouse.

But, most curious of all, I have received a positive spate of invitations to put pen to paper and write letters of advice, encouragement and approbation to a variety of scum of whose existence I am only dimly aware.

Who is this Prince Edward chappie?

And why ask me to get him an introduction to Cliff Richard?

Why should I bother my backside with Princess Michael of the Huns and her troubles?

If she wants to take over 'Wish You Were Here' from Judith Chalmers, that's her business.

Enough.

Let us accept our new-found fame 'as it comes'.

Let us bask briefly while we can in its warm glow.

Let us present to you, dear readers, two of the dispatches I have recently penned.

LETTER NUMBER ONE:

A letter of advice to a vague acquaintance whose grandson is about to undertake a school cricket tour to the West Indies.

My dear Monsignor.
Greetings from Witney Scrotum.

I am informed by that emaciated vileness, Tinniswood, that the chaps are about to undertake a tour of cricketing bent to the twin islands of Trinidad and Tobago.

Congratters!

I heartily approve.

Working their passage before the mast on a leaking Estonian Cape Horner will do wonders for their characters and discourage the male pubescent's tendency to comport himself in a manner reminiscent of Sir Andrew Lloyd-Webster on heat.

Fending for themselves in the tropical jungles will undoubtedly teach them the virtues of stealth and duplicity which are essential requirements should they wish in later life to assume careers as schoolmasters or personal press officers to the incumbent at Number Ten.

I envy them deeply for all the ghastly privations and hardships they will undoubtedly suffer in those God-forsaken, fever-ridden, typhoon-blasted islands with ne'er a sniff of a Boots gift token or a sight of a Harris tweed sports jacket.

However I offer several words of warning.

On the ablutions front it is essential in tropical climes, as in the smoking rooms of the House of Commons, to pay particular attention to every aspect of personal cleanliness.

Fresh running water and Michael Heseltine autograph drip mats will be at a premium and I, therefore, recommend before setting forth from the shores of our beloved and blessed island nation that the chaps are thoroughly fumigated for nits, body lice and armpit rot and immersed for at least three days in their local car wash prior to embarkation.

For complete safety I would advise that they shave their private parts, cork their navels with tallow and daub themselves liberally with Trevor Bailey sleeping sickness ointment.

Provender: Do not, chaps, at any price touch the local food, which consists almost entirely of desiccated bush hats, regurgitated menus from mobile Cunard ocean liners and parboiled English Test batsmen's unmentionables.

The Inhabitants: In the main the inhabitants of Trinidad are a friendly crowd much addicted to the novels of Mrs Gaskell and the later string quartets of Bela Bartok.

Most of them are direct descendants of an unofficial liaison between Dr W.G. Grace and Miss Frances Edmonds (as she likes to be called) and thus both sexes are heavily bearded and congenitally flat-footed.

Incidentally, if any of the chaps should contemplate marriage to the more nubile female members of the population, I would recommend that they write immediately under plain cover to Mr Philip Tufnell, who himself lives in a plain cover envelope these days.

Clothing: It is the custom in Trinidad and Tobago to walk around naked in public places until the hour of sundown.

If the chaps should wish to follow the practice (and why not?), I earnestly implore them to consider their position vis-à-vis walking through the swing doors of authorised launderettes and sessions of lunchtime sequence dancing with stokers from the royal yacht.

Never wear spats in the presence of chartered accountants and remember that, as in the House of Commons debating chamber, sessions of public onanism are not frowned upon.

Finally, chaps, I can recommend a most discreet tattoo parlour in one of the more salubrious districts of Port of Spain, where for a mere fifty-five pence you can have your body completely covered with multi-coloured representations of Mr Jonathan Agnew at toilet and President Mitterand cutting his toenails in the Channel Tunnel.

I wish you well.

Have a thoroughly ripping time and remember that you are the true sons of post-Thatcherite Britain – always say No at times of deepest temptation.

And if that doesn't work, say Yes.

LETTER NUMBER TWO:

A missive to a certain Gordon Samuel Gray Esquire of Congleton on the occasion of the Benson and Hedges Cup encounter between Cheshire and Durham at Bowdon in the fair county of Cheshire.

My dear Gray,

Greetings from Witney Scrotum.

I am pleased to record that all is well with the world hereabouts.

We have just successfully concluded our annual Festival of Nose Picking and Making Rude Noises in the Bath.

That emaciated vileness, Tinniswood, was the winner

in both competitions and also scored heavily in the handicap race for self-propelled underpants.

Guest of honour was the delectable Miss Joanna Lumley, who most graciously consented to bring her teeth with her in two large Securicor armed pantechnicons, and to our great delight came a creditable second in the Dick Pollard Lookalike contest.

On the natural history front we have had some notable triumphs.

Our local ornithologist and honorary toad circumciser, Oslear, reported sightings of the rare long-tailed Tattersall's godwit and the shy Pullar's flightless rail on the water meadows at Cowdrey's Bottom.

And on the summit of the towering buttress of Botham's Gut he has discovered firm evidence of the first successful breeding in the British Isles of the one-legged ostrich.

But enough of these boastings.

I pen these words to congratulate everyone concerned on the staging at Bowdon of what I am sure will be a most fruitful indoor lacrosse match between Cheshire and Durham.

Contrary to popular belief I have always felt a close affinity with the peoples of the North Country.

I admire their fortitude.

I praise their resolution.

It must be simply ghastly having to use outside privies in the depths of a bleak Northern winter with icicles dripping from your mangles and naught to wipe your backsides on save back numbers of the *Sunday Empire News*.

It must be horrendous having to survive on a daily

diet of stirrup pump soup, boiled bolster cases and laxative pyjama cords.

And God knows how you manage to cope with the bands of marauding footpads and ex-Hanoverian mercenaries in the dark, festering alleyways of Ashton-on-Mersey.

But do not give in.

There is always light at the end of the tunnel.

I am certain that one fine day you will be visited by missionaries from Romford and Basildon bearing gifts of Vick inhalers and novelty magnets.

I am convinced that in time United Nations relief lorries will manage to negotiate the perils and dangers of Lymm Corner to bring you emergency supplies of Donald Duck toothbrushes and inflatable piano stools.

I want you to know that you are all 'dear to our hearts'.

Here in Witney Scrotum you are constantly in our thoughts.

In the parish church of St Kevin de Keegan (patron saint of damp sibilants and home perms) dear old Grannie Swanton lights specially hand-knitted, non-stick pipe cleaners in your memory.

In our local hostelry, the Jug and Arlott, mine host, Statham, has instituted a collection for the relief of your starving children under the banner 'Rickets Anonymous'.

I am pleased to report that to date he has collected three second-hand Marmite labels, a half-scale working model of Sir John Barbirolli's left testicle and the egg cup used as a hip bath by the Japanese ambassador to the Court of St James.

I myself personally am seriously considering donating the remote control buttons off the Lady Wife's mobile commode.

Be brave, my dear friends.

Show courage.

You cannot help being Northerners.

It is not your fault.

There is always hope that one glorious day you will wake up speaking with a Birmingham accent and remembering not to stick your fingers in the light sockets.

PS: That emaciated vileness, Tinniswood, who was brought up in Cheshire and for some unknown reason takes enormous pride from that fact, sends his adopted county his fondest good wishes.

If I were a Cestrian faced with that burden, I should immediately cover myself with fossilised rabbit tods and tram drivers' dandruff and pretend I was crown prince of Altrincham.

CHAPTER THREE

Slakehouse

I should not like it to be thought that we are bigots here in our beloved Witney Scrotum.

Neither are we gripped in the relentless, vice-like arms of blind prejudice.

We show as much regard and toleration as every one of our fellow countrymen for the slack-jawed, booze-bellied Northern working-class scum, who clog our motorways with their vile, garish Japanese fart boxes and despoil vast tracts of unsullied virgin countryside with their ghastly mobile caravanettes constructed in stoop-shouldered, pigeon-chested, reeking back yards out of disused sardine tins and reconstituted dog kennels.

In matters pertaining to the great and burning issues of the day we are equally tolerant.

Our attitude to women priests is exactly the same as it is to their male colleagues – perfectly acceptable provided they do not wear false eyelashes and conceal beneath their surplices French suspenders and black silk stockings.

We believe implicitly in the public flogging of sullen dry cleaners, small children with runny noses and bus conductors who eat with their mouths open.

We enthusiastically support instant garrotting and sub-sequent deportation for anyone caught trying to conduct the orchestra from the front row of the audience during televised transmissions of BBC Promenade Concerts.

We are steadfast in our backing for those who propose the imposition of compulsory thrice daily cold baths for Pakistani Test cricketers, not one of whom, incidentally, has ever been tampered with in the purlieus of our village.

On the topic of sport we hold similar catholic views.

We do not wear blinkers.

We do not bury our heads in the sand.

We are not solely devoted to cricket.

We have all expressed the desire to leap over the barriers and rugby tackle Messrs Torvill and Dean as they perform their grisly sequin-encrusted moving gyrations.

We have never disguised our strong and sincere longing to pull out the toenails and nasal hairs of professional snooker players with Woolworth bulldog clips, nobble the feed of lady three-day eventers with quick-acting laxatives and stick extremely large carrots up the bottoms of all those taking part in the University Boat Race.

Never shall I forget that glorious evening of recent blessed memory when the whole village was gathered round their respective moving television sets, cheering on Linford Christie as he won the women's hop, step and jump mixed relay in the Gateshead Olympic Games at some place whose name I did not quite catch.

How the brute deserved his success.

I have personally sent him a five shillings postal order and trust he will 'put it to good use'.

In similar vein we at Witney Scrotum have nothing but the deepest sympathy for those poor, blighted souls who seem to spend a considerable part of their waking hours attempting to propel an oversized white vitamin pill down the bottom of a miniature flagpole with nothing to aid them but a collection of severely misshapen walking sticks.

As proof of our liberal attitude on these matters I offer you the example of Slakehouse.

Slakehouse is an elderly gentleman of obvious Northern extraction who lives in our village under an upturned zinc bath in the back yard of the cricket bag repository.

What other village, I ask you earnestly, would tolerate the presence in its midst of a wizened, moth-infested, fetid, belching, terminal inebriate with congenitally unbuttoned flies and a yellowing tongue encrusted with what appears to be a full set of aged rusting mountaineers' crampons?

Who is he?

What is he?

No, he is not an ITN newscaster 'down on his luck'.

No, he is not a former financial adviser to the Duchess of York.

No, he is not a younger version of Mr Ned Sherrin.

The answer is far more potent and pungent – he is, dear readers, a sportsman.

And thus is he welcome in our village.

How and when did he arrive in Witney Scrotum?

On the matter of date we cannot be precise.

But then neither can Mr Raymond Illingworth be certain of the date on which he last captained Yorkshire from his bath chair.

And Sir Geoffrey Boycott is in a sea of total confusion regarding the date on which he is to have the next mammogram on his wallet under local anaesthetic.

However, on the circumstances of Slakehouse's arrival in Witney Scrotum we can be slightly more accurate.

The event took place at 7.13 am on the morning of 17 May 1959.

The sun was shining timidly.

Larks were soaring.

Coot were splashing in ferny fronds.

Over the tranquil rooftops rose the lulling, lilting scents of old Grannie Swanton's bonfire as she slow-roasted the Tufnell twins in compliance with their most recent probation order.

And then quite without warning Slakehouse appeared, dragging himself down the main street in the most piteous and heart-rending condition, begging for food, water and antique snuff boxes.

The village rallied round to him instantly and magnificently.

Without demur Miss Roebuck from the dog biscuit shop handed him half a dozen millet sprays and two sachets of worming powder.

Gooch, the blacksmith, was swift to share with him his breakfast of iron filings junket and leggings cutlets.

PC 'Percy' Pocock arranged for him to take liquid refreshment from the village horse trough as soon as the scum had returned to the surface.

And old Squire Brearley with typical kindly generosity presented him with half a dozen of his pamphlets on the Hanseatic League and its influence on egg custard.

On such provender did Slakehouse prosper and in 'next to no time' become a valued and much-cherished member of our community.

Over the intervening years I have got to know him tolerably well.

From time to time I make it my business to visit him in his dank, snuffling, reeking abode and there, keeping well down wind, I toss him bags of bones and the occasional packet of half-sucked Locketts.

At other times, wearing a surgeon's face mask, industrial gauntlets and heavy-duty carpet slippers, I have conversed with him.

And from these talks I have gleaned 'something about him', the details of which I now propose to share with you, dear readers.

Let us plunge straight to the heart of the matter.

It transpires that John Boynton Slakehouse is none other than Britain's first professional road race unicycle champion.

Imagine my exultation and my radiance of spirit when I first discovered this information.

My plus fours throbbed.

My stumper's mallet rose unaided to stiff attention.

I had hot flushes in my smoker's compendium.

Thus must Sir Richard Burton have felt, when after years of arduous and fever-wracked wanderings, he first set eyes on the Manchester Ship Canal.

Thus must Miss Joanna Lumley have felt when she grew her third pair of teeth.

Thus must . . .

No, let us not allow our imagination and our fancies to run riot.

Rather let us apply our minds to the beginnings of Gilbert Keith Slakehouse's glorious and distinguished career.

The infant David Herbert Slakehouse was born into conditions of extreme poverty in the dark recesses of deepest industrial Lancashire within sight of the harsh, forbidding Tattersall Moors and the sluggish headwaters of the River Pollard.

'Hard commons' was the perpetual lot of the family and only on rare occasions were they able to purchase fresh quails' eggs, second-hand black puddings, and hand-me-down meat and potato pies.

Often they were compelled to 'make do' with laver bread gleaned from the used hankies of itinerant Welsh whippet trainers.

Indeed so poor were they that they could not afford two wheels for their bicycles and were thus forced to make do with one.

As Slakehouse puts it so succinctly and so movingly:

'I were right lucky really because when I were born, unicycling were in the blood.'

And so were any other facets of the world of cycling.

His father, Pelham Grenville Slakehouse, spent long, crutch-shrivelling winter nights sticking miniature puncture outfits into stone hot water bottles for sale in the local market at Cardus-in-Tyldesleydale.

His mother earned a few meagre extra coppers, darning tyre levers for the local gentry.

And his eldest sister was often forced at times of direst need to pose nude save for gear lever and bicycle clips for L.S. Lowry, some of whose paintings may be seen to this day displayed in a place of honour in the Long Room at Lord's.

It is no surprise, therefore, to learn that our hero commenced his career at a very tender age indeed, when his parents strapped him to the wheel of his grandmother's mangle in an attempt to stop him eating his father's saddle bag.

Within weeks the miracle occurred – the young Herbert George Slakehouse had learnt to pedal!

After this it was but a short time until he graduated to the wheel on top of the pithead winding gear.

Day after day he was to be seen strapped to the wheel by his uncle's muffler and his auntie's razor strop, pedalling away like a dervish.

It wasn't long before he was strong enough to be able to pull up cages of men from the night shift completely unaided.

The steam engine was declared redundant and henceforth the young Slakehouse became the pit's sole source of motive power.

In off duty hours in order to earn extra money to support his mother's addiction to ball bearings he would strap himself to the generator in the local electricity works and thus through his efforts were the delights of the moving kinema brought to his humble village.

There are those who maintain that, had the National Grid been in existence at the time, he could have provided enough electricity to power the entire wind section of the Hallé Orchestra with a bit left over for Mr Maurice Denham's novelty lifts at Broadcasting House, which to this very day are wont to trap the noses of those unwary enough to share the vehicle with Miss Libby Purves.

It was from these activities that he acquired all those strengths and skills which made him an ideal candidate for the spartan life of a professional unicyclist.

His first success came at the age of sixteen shortly after his underpants reached the age of puberty, when he won the Bolton to Rochdale Classic in the record time of two years and three months.

But he soon tired of these sprint races and turned his attentions to the more satisfying and challenging long distance events.

Over the years a string of successes followed, too numerous to mention here.

Then came the ultimate triumph – the championship of the world.

This took place in 1922 over the infamous Transalpine course with its dizzy drops, its throat-choking hairpins and its marauding bands of starving Swan Hellenic couriers.

Slakehouse took all these dangers 'in his stride' and won in the extraordinary time of thirty-seven years and two days.

It beat the previous record by three seconds.

This race, has, of course, gone down in the annals of unicycling history.

There were thirty-eight competitors and George Bernard Slakehouse was the only man to finish.

'It was,' he says, 'a catalogue of bloody disasters.'

Seventeen of his rivals died during the course of the race.

With some it was a simple case of advanced senility.

With others it was the untimely intervention of the Second World War, three being killed in a Lancaster bombing raid on Stuttgart and two meeting their end through the agency of an infected Ack Ack gun in Aldershot.

There were other unfortunate interjections.

At least ten of the competitors got married and during the normal course of events that attend the marital status became chronic shoplifters, recidivist arsonists and professional footballers with Manchester United.

In addition one competitor underwent a sex change operation and was thus disqualified for losing his cross bar.

Yet another became Prime Minister of Italy, commenting afterwards that it was the most satisfying ten minutes of his life.

But Slakehouse's triumph was tempered by sadness when after those long years he returned to his home village bearing his trophy with pride.

Time had taken its toll and not a single villager recognised the home-coming hero.

The pithead had gone. The mill chimneys had been pulled down.

The street corner pubs had been turned into pubic toupe parlours and all he could see was an endless vista of unisex estate agents and self-service tropical fish emporiums.

And so with misery and despair deep in his tired old heart he set off on a trail of rootless wanderings until eventually he found himself here in Witney Scrotum.

He bears no malice.

He has no regrets.

He is indeed a happy and contented man.

One day after I had presented him with a batch of condemned rusks, I asked him:

'Have you any further ambitions in life, Slakehouse?'

'Aye,' he said. 'I have that.'

'And what are they, old chap?' I said.

He looked me straight in the eye and said without prompting:

'To be buried in a unicoffin.'

Dear, dear, precious Wystan Hugh Slakehouse.

CHAPTER FOUR

Himmelweit Revisited

You will recall, no doubt, dear readers, the singular history of Himmelweit, the only German ever to play first class county cricket.

For those who have not been paying attention I shall explain briefly.

Himmelweit came to this blessed country of ours in the year 1916 when his Zeppelin was shot down during a bombing raid on Shepton Mallet – thus giving him instant residential qualifications to play for Somerset.

He was deposited forthwith into prison – thus giving him residential qualifications to play for Wormwood Scrubs, which he did with considerable distinction, scoring an undefeated 'ton' in the late August of 1918 against an Old Harrovians Transvestites' Select.

At the end of hostilities he came to the attention of 'the authorities' whilst playing in a Victory Celebration match, Minor Counties versus The Huns, in which in the company of Mr Bertolt Brecht he shared an opening partnership of 227.

He was recruited immediately by Somerset, where his career blossomed and bloomed until the notorious 'Incident at Frome' involving among other things an unauthorised toad circumciser's bradawl, a German cavalryman's spiked helmet and three unexploded trench mortar shells.

Whilst incidents of this sort would be considered of minor importance during an annual meeting of the Yorkshire County Cricket Club, Himmelweit was deemed by his adopted country to have 'let the side down' and thus, as rumour has it, was taken by a detachment of the Somerset Light Yeomanry and Semi Mobile Hussars at dead of night to London, where he was summarily executed at the rear of the real tennis courts at Lord's.

So the matter has rested for more than half a century, regarded as nothing more than a curious footnote in the historic annals of our beloved 'summer game'.

But now I fear the records have to be rewritten and 'put straight'.

I am loath to bring distress to those still extant (and indeed those decidedly non-extant like the governing body of MCC) who still remember Himmelweit's strident appealing in his native German *'Wie ist Das?'* and his taking guard at the wicket with the words *'Mittel und Bein'*.

However, I feel I have a duty to the game I adore and worship and whose continued good reputation is paramount for the survival of all that we hold dear in these benighted times when the Prime Ministership of this country is held by a creature with all the charm and charisma of an occasional third seamer for Lincolnshire.

I have consulted on this matter with Mr E.W. 'Gloria' Swanton, currently honorary chaplain to Mr Billy J. Kramer and the Dakotas, and he concurs most wholeheartedly in these sentiments.

My story starts thus:

To my intense horror the Lady Wife with her piggy little eyes and equine yellowing teeth insisted that we spend Christmas with distant friends at their residence in the South of France, 'The Villa Gimblett'.

Imagine my distress, dear readers.

Being dragged away from the dear familiar Yuletide delights of Witney Scrotum with the joyous bonfires fizzing and sparking on the massive buttresses of the great earthwork of Botham's Gut, the annual ritual of deflowering our resident mobile librarians (non-fiction section) on the water meadows of Cowdrey's Bottom and that magical, mystical moment in the parish church one minute before the anniversary of Our Saviour's Birth when the whole village gathers round the Jack Crapp Memorial reredos to stick fretwork toothpicks into a wax effigy of Mr H.D. 'Dicky' Bird – truly a fate worse than death – or, ghastlier still, an evening spent in the company of Yorkshire's answer to Barbara Cartland, Mr Raymond Illingworth.

And for what?

I'll tell you for what – a week in foreign, dago-infested climes with naught to succour the eyes but shimmering blue seas, relentless azure skies, shy cool courtyards tinkling with the gentle sputter of crystal clear water and raven-haired, bold-breasted young women with scavenging thighs who would have been better employed trying to get decent reception of the BBC World Service on the talking wireless.

Scum and trash, the whole lot of them.

I confess I was in low spirits after a Christmas luncheon which to my untutored palate seemed to consist of reconstituted cricket bags stuffed with garlic-flavoured fast bowlers' socks followed by compote of umpires' hankies and cheese the consistency and taste of the handle of a scorer's briefcase.

To my amazement, however, the Lady Wife, seeing my profound distress, took pity on me and suggested we take an afternoon stroll.

Anything was better than listening to our host playing the late tone poems of Emmot 'Stanford' Robinson on his Barnsley bagpipes and so I eagerly agreed to her suggestion.

Out we stepped on to alien cobbles basking under a snickering, conceited sun.

Slowly we trudged up an alien hill contorted with thickets of olives and glowing lemon trees mocking my consort's Safeway's plastic shopping carrier, which contained her antidago spray and her fumigation ointment for application to strange menus.

At length we passed through a small, creaking iron gate and entered an overgrown cemetery.

Good God, I thought, fancy the dagos having the impertinence to die like us.

Bastards.

Further thoughts on the essential impermanence of the human condition and the imminence of an impending Biggies were dispelled when the Lady Wife stopped dead in her tracks.

'Look,' she said. 'Look.'

I looked in the direction indicated by the toe of her left hiking boot.

And there I saw it.

A small headstone.

I bent down and read its inscription.

'Himmelweit. Uhlan and County Cricketer. 1898–1984. *Gott sei Dank.*'

'Who's this blighter Gott sei Dank he's buried with?' I said.

Before the Lady Wife could answer, a figure stepped out from behind a gaunt, brooding cyprus.

It was bent and cavernous of chest, the nose end festooned with icy stalactites of gilberts, the shin bones creaking, the wind sighing mournfully through its emaciated ribcage.

But I knew its identity at once.

The duelling scar, the glinting monocle, the unsheathed sabre, the faded blue cricket cap emblazoned with the winged dragon of Somerset – yes, it was Himmelweit, and he was wearing Peter Roebuck's socks.

The poor, desperate creature broke into unrestrained sobbing when he saw my MCC cufflinks and my I Zingari collar stiffeners.

Such was his inconsolable distress that we were compelled to help him to a nearby café where we seated him at a table in the lee of a signed aquatint of Miss Alma Cogan and offered him liquid refreshment.

'*Vin du pays?*' said the proprietor, a shifty-looking brute with unshaven shirt front and hostile armpits.

'Well, I'd rather pay than have the vin,' I said. 'But I suppose beggars can't be choosers.'

We were presented with a bottle of liquid which to my untutored eyes looked the colour of a heavily-sucked Northamptonshire CCC cricket cap, but from which Himmelweit drank copious quantities, wiping his mouth on the disposable linoleum which covered the floor.

And presently as the warmth returned to his body and the colour to his sunken cheeks he told his story.

It was indeed a sorry tale.

With typical Teutonic vileness and lack of gratitude he had escaped the exigencies of the firing squad and fled to the South of France.

There he had eked out a precarious living first as a batting coach to Mr Somerset Maugham, then as rounders consultant to Sir Harold Acton and latterly as instructor in the more abstruse and non-combatant of martial arts to Mr Noël Coward.

After the death of whom he termed 'The Master', a soubriquet I had always thought applied to Mr Richie Benaud, he had temporarily captained a cricket team of expatriate British aesthetes and bon vivants, the Twee Foresters, and then had come dire and abject poverty.

'But what about this blasted headstone of yours, you odious Teutonic stinker?' I said.

He sighed and shrugged his shoulders.

Through the means of his Wisden's German–English dictionary and much sign language of a deeply offensive nature he explained that with typical Germanic thoroughness he had bought it on his arrival on the Côte d'Azure and positioned it secure in the knowledge that he would have a permanent resting place when his innings drew to a close in 1984.

'But, damn you, sir, it's 1995 now,' I said.

Once more he sighed.

'I know,' he said. 'That was always my trouble. No one ever knew how to get me out.'

He excused himself and shuffled off to the gents' urinals, a structure which to my untutored eyes looked more like the ladies' pavilion at Old Trafford than an ablutions parlour fit for men of the crimson rambler and the silken willow.

'Right,' said the Lady Wife firmly. 'Right.'

Before I could stop her she had stood up, extracted my portable stumper's mallet from the inside pocket of my blazer and marched off in the direction taken by Himmelweit.

Five minutes later she returned.

Alone.

'Right then,' she said. 'It's done. I've given him out.'

Carefully she wiped the head of my stumper's mallet on the corner of the tablecloth and replaced it into my pocket.

'Good God,' I croaked. 'You haven't . . . You can't possibly have . . .'

'Yes,' said the Lady Wife. 'And there's no need to worry. I remembered to shake his Thingie before I did the dirty deed.'

I nodded.

I sighed with contentment.

With an epitaph such as that, I thought, a man can indeed rest secure in the lonely vastness of Eternity.

CHAPTER FIVE

In Dock

The golden fob watch of the sun beams from the brim of Botham's Gut.

The River Buse waddles slow and stately through the reedy rush of the misting valley.

Shire horses whinny and flare their fetlocks in the buttercupped water meadows at Cowdrey's Bottom.

Woodpecking yaffle.

Nightjarring chur.

Rode of woodcock.

The craking corn and the creaking barn.

All is well with the world.

All is benign and silly with summer stars.

Yet I feel a deep sense of unease and disquiet.

The spittle tastes sour in the bowl of my pipe. My socks itch. My cufflinks glower sullenly. Listless and lethargic are the fly buttons on my old plus fours.

I have an urgent question to ask of you, dear readers.

It is this:

What is the worst possible fate that can befall a man of a 'cricketing bent'?

Being compelled to attend a demonstration of mass breast-feeding by Italian waitresses in Dunoon?

Spending the weekend alone in a Birkenhead boarding house with Mussolini and Javed Miandad?

Having Mr Fred Rumsey sit on your knee during an entire performance of *Die Meistersinger*?

Watching Mr Merv Hughes eating a packet of Rice Crispies through a snorkel?

Ghastly enough these penances are, my friends, but there is one punishment grislier by far to all dedicated devotees of our beloved 'summer game'.

It is this:

Being compelled to visit the Lady Wife in hospital on the Saturday of the Lord's Test.

This lamentable commission was inflicted on me only last week, and I confess that I am still reeling from its effects despite three days of intensive bathing in hot Lemsip and an emergency Hobday operation at our local equine rehabilitation centre.

The circumstances were thus:

The Lady Wife had placed herself 'in dock' for her annual MOT.

Apart from slight trouble with her tappets and an insistent grumbling in her automatic transmission she had been pronounced 'fit for anything' by her personal quack and home hairdresser, Doctor 'La Serenissima' Bottomley.

Typically, however, she insisted on extending her stay in hospital, pleading an aversion to the smell of my pipe in her pyjama case and the unexplained presence of hamster droppings in the bottom of the Lloyd loom linen baskets.

Thus did she once again make near terminal inroads into my medical insurance policy taken out many years previously under the auspices of the Scottish Widows and Minor Counties Umpires Mutual Benefit Friendly Society.

And thus it was that full of foreboding and stale rum I sallied forth in the trusty, navy blue Lanchester to visit her in hospital in the company of the Commodore and my dearest chum, my precious, saintly 'Bruce' Woodcock of *The Times* printed newspaper, who in honour of the occasion was wearing his new raspberry-ripple, quick-release jump suit and a most bewitching pair of Gunn and Moore canary yellow jazz pumps.

The villagers greeted us fondly as we drove slowly down the main street of Witney Scrotum.

Miss Roebuck from the dog biscuit shop strewed our path with Spiller's shapes and aniseed-flavoured flea collars.

Old Grannie Swanton took time off from defusing the German incendiary bomb in her front garden to doff her tin helmet and cry 'Hurrah' three times.

The Reverend Gwilliam Loften-Jones of The Church of The Third Wicket Down Redemption dashed out from his corrugated iron chapel and garlanded our roof rack with posies of Welsh poppies and joyously bit great chunks out of our mudguards.

The outward journey was uneventful.

We forced three RAC patrolmen to 'take cover' on the by-pass outside Keating New Town.

We 'put the wind up' an armoured tank carrier on the bridge at Dredge's Elbow.

We caused 'severe delays' to a funeral cortège in an uncharted underpass in the main street of Warminster.

And, of course, we refreshed ourselves at a multitude of watering holes where we knew we would be greeted with affection and approbation by landladies with big noses and not be compelled to send out scouting parties in search of non-stick toilet paper.

In one of the hostelries concerned we had a minor distraction, owing to the Commodore's contretemps with a matting wicket dispenser in the snug bar urinals, which resulted in the emergency call-out of the volunteer fire brigade, who managed to release him by application of the latest technique in natural childbirth – the so-called 'Gatting Reverse Sweep' system.

It was dusk by the time we reached our destination.

Owls were hooting.

Bats were flitting.

Hedgehogs snuffled and shuffled and all over the land drink-crazed swimming bath attendants snored, replete in their lovers' beds.

And dear old 'Bruce' Woodcock was hiccuping softly in the back seat of the trusty Lanchester, a jumbo-sized bottle of stoat gin clasped to his chest, and on his knee a Wensleydale tup which had mysteriously insinuated itself into our company 'somewhere along the way' was gently licking the boil plasters on his ankles.

The Commodore selflessly volunteered to remain in the car to look after our chum and ensure that, when he awoke, he would not be tempted to 'experiment' with the self-lighting cigar lighter on the front dashboard, an action which some years previously had resulted in his long and painful incarceration for six months in the Benson and Hedges research and hospitality tent at the Cheltenham Festival.

After this experience 'Bruce' averred that he thoroughly enjoyed the company of the laboratory rats but 'didn't think much' to the propinquity of the double-glazing salesmen.

And thus it was that I set off alone on the long and perilous passage to the Lady Wife's presence, a journey to compare with the vilest ravages of misery, despair and dan-

gers experienced by Pizarro and Magellan, by Speke and
Burton, by Burke and Wills or, worse by far, by Harris and
Keeton, making their way to the wicket to open the innings
at five forty-seven of a gloomy evening on the second day's
play at Worksop.

Once inside the hospital I encountered a hunch-
shouldered creature, flat-footed, hollow-cheeked, festooned
in copper bangles, padding lugubriously down the corridors,
dressed in white cap, white boots and white knee-length
coat.

'What-ho, Dickie,' I said. 'I thought you were supposed
to be standing at Melton Mowbray today.'

The brute turned to me, growled most fearfully, rattled
his portable stethoscope and threatened me with instant
shaving in the nether regions of the popping crease.

I confess that had the creature indeed been Mr H.D.
'Dickie' Bird, I should have immediately accepted his kind
invitation, but as he bore all the facial characteristics of the
resident sick berth attendant of the BBC talking wireless
ball-by-ball commentary team, I declined his invitation and
made 'my excuses' in the manner of Mr Jonathan Agnew
interviewing Miss Joan Collins in the umpires' *salle privée*
at Hove.

I own that the nurses were 'kindness personified' in
directing me to the Lady Wife's quarters.

Sister Lewis fluttered her dark-drooping, Celtic eyelids
at me and offered to show me her tele-prompt, provided I
promised not to look in her handbag.

Staff Nurse Benaud, all sheer black stockings and
Vegemite-flavoured lipstick, volunteered to cut my
toenails with her own personal teeth – or anyone else's,
come to that.

And Matron Lamb made incomprehensible whirring and grunting noises from her position halfway up my shins and showed me the native baubles she had acquired during her winter sojourn in South Africa, where she had assisted most nobly in the world's first helmet transplant on Herr Kepler Wessels.

For this she had been awarded the iron cross third class and a course in basic elocution at the Central School of Drama and Speech Therapy.

'Oim so plissed – it's worked winders,' she said. 'Oim uver de min.'

There was a brief interlude whilst I ate twenty-nine fish and chip suppers with the chief dietitian, Dr 'Flat Jack' Simmons, and then I could postpone it no longer – I had to meet the Lady Wife.

Her first words were:

'What's all this? What the devil is all this rubbish you've brought?'

And in a swift and violent movement of her massive, Voce-like fist she swept to the floor all the gifts I had so laboriously and diligently gathered for her delectation and enjoyment.

In the subsequent bout of ferocious heavy breathing I surveyed sadly the booty of my slight affection towards my spouse as it cowered on the floor at the foot of her bed – the thirty-seven back numbers of *The Cricketer*, the miniature metal detector, the eleven tins of pemmican, the bills from British Telecom and the Wessex Running Water Authority, the summons from the county court for non-payment of council tax and the remains of her silver fox stole savaged in a moment of bored idleness by her loathsome Bedlington terriers.

Why such outrage?

Why such ferocity of mien?

I could easily have brought for her approval the corpse of the coypu which only that very morning I had discovered lying peacefully among the shattered porcelain of her display cabinet.

The Lady Wife glowered at me.

Thus had the Teutonic Knights cast their haughty sneers over the cowering Letts.

Thus had the warriors of Characene curled their wicked cold-rimmed lips at the fleeing hordes of Seleucids.

Thus had Curtly Ambrose gazed down upon poor, stricken Jack Russell.

Silence.

At length I attempted to make conversation.

'I see Durham are making a hash of things again,' I said.

Silence.

Silence, shimmering there in the helpless gloom, screaming mutely at the faint billow of the curtains.

I tried again.

'The piano tuner called this morning. Shall I nip out and buy a piano?'

Silence once more.

Total, impenetrable silence like taking breakfast with the Bedser twins at the YMCA, Nuneaton, or listening to Mr Keith Fletcher's appraisal of a Teddy Tail colouring book.

Yet again I tried.

'Do you think Mavis in "Coronation Street" is any good at badminton?' I said.

Silence.

Utter silence.

And then, dear readers, oh, bliss of bliss – soft snores.

Carefully I prised myself out of the Lady Wife's commode, into which I had inadvertently taken station, and bent over her bed.

Yes, she was sound asleep, looking for all the world like a Brisbane 'sticky dog'.

I have to confess it – feelings of a distinctly carnal nature commenced to flood through my spinning finger.

How I should have liked to apply the Trent Bridge heavy roller to her radiant torso.

How I should have loved to apply a top dressing of Norfolk marl to her noble chest.

How I should have adored to sprinkle her from head to foot with the hosepipe from our beloved Bramall Lane.

But no.

Reason prevailed.

And after popping three generous fingers of Lock and Laker arch-support rum into the Lady Wife's saline drip I returned to my companions.

Ah, the blessed relief of it all.

Normality greeted me like a fawning Newfoundland retriever or a Derbyshire medium-pace seamer joyously rolling in aged cowpats in the outfield at Buxton.

Dear old 'Bruce' Woodcock had once more most amusingly set light to his shirt tail and the Commodore was busily barbecuing the seat belts of the trusty old Lanchester for supper.

On the journey home I was beset with fancies of the choicest kind.

If, by some misfortune, I were to be placed 'in dock', which visitor would I most like to receive at my bedside?

Terry Venables?

No.

He'd most likely pick me to play goalkeeper for England.

Herbert von Karajan?

No.

He'd probably stick his baton up my nose.

Prince Charles?

No.

How would I know when he had left?

And then it came to me.

Got it.

The very man.

Barbara Dixon.

Dame Barbara Dixon, the paragon of all female virtues – fond of cricket but 'knows her place', singer of songs, but not too many.

I was carried away by my passions.

I had visions of opening the bowling with her for Minor Counties versus Sri Lanka.

I had dreams of sharing a last wicket stand with her for the Club Cricket Conference versus the Bassetlaw League.

I had fantasies of slowly and sensuously peeling off her thigh pads at . . .

But then reason prevailed.

On the outskirts of Swindon we ran into a lawn mower shop.

I was placed 'in dock' for three days.

I had but one visitor.

She did not say who she was.

CHAPTER SIX

Mitchell Dever

He was a portly man.

Portly.

Damn fine word, portly.

Disguises a multitude of sins and omissions. Brings a warm flush to the haggard, wasted, gaunt cheeks of distant happiness.

Squats like a fat buck rabbit in the cramped, draughty hutch of rebuff and defeat.

He was a portly man with jowls.

Jowls.

Damn fine word, jowls.

Warms the throat of the razored wind from the east. Soothes the chapped, rasping kisses of meagre passions.

He was a portly man with jowls and he carried a portly, jowled Gladstone bag, creaking at its clasps and giddy with faded constellations of hotel labels from distant climes.

He wore a pearl grey Anthony Eden hat and an ankle-length, mustard and maroon check overcoat voluminous enough to give shelter from the elements to a weekend retreat of bookmakers' runners.

On his feet were brown plimsolls with shiny black, rubber toecaps.

He had a nose like a cluster of angry radishes.

His moustache was the size and shape of a long-abandoned ginger tom cat.

It had a similar smell when exposed to hang-dog gas fires.

Thin strands of jet black hair were greased unlovingly across a balding pate and protruded over the back of his rumpled collar like porcupine quills.

His name was Mitchell Dever and every year on the first Sunday of the toad-baiting season he would come to Witney Scrotum to take up residence in the guest room of the Jug and Arlott.

Mitchell Dever – the most famous, the most celebrated, the most legendary sports writer in the whole history of printed newspapers.

Mitchell Dever – known to colleagues, rivals and hoarse-bosomed barmaids alike as 'The First Gentleman of Fleet Street'.

Why did he come here each year?

No one knew.

For three long weeks he would incarcerate himself under lock and key in the gangly-curtained, pock-plastered guest room of the Jug and Arlott, and not a soul in the village caught sight nor light of him.

We would hear the clump and slut of clumsy feet, the painful rasp of retchy coughs, the clinking of complaining bottles and the laboured movement of heavy furniture over our heads as we sat in the snug bar drinking pints of Farmer Emburey's untreated, non-medicinal, pre-vintage scrumpy.

And sometimes there would be the sounds of high-pitched clickings and long mournful grunts and sighs like the love songs of stricken whales and Derbyshire leg spinners.

We all had our theories for his solitary sojourn in our village.

Squire Brearley said he was convalescing from a chronic attack of hyperbole and a severe dose of litotes and metathesis.

Old Grannie Swanton said he had the clap.

Dear Miss Roebuck from the dog biscuit shop was convinced he was a war lord from the white slave traffic, and, oh, how she would adore to be whisked away in an Arab dhow to a tasselled desert tent where she would recline on silken cushions in a shift of shimmering, transparent muslin, and cool-navelled negro slaves would lick the soles of her feet with glistening-pink, salamander tongues and a Bedouin sheik with scimitar nose and daggered eyes would crush her to his throbbing loins and never ever again would she need to secrete under her lime green mohair twinset much-thumbed, slim, light novellas from the Romance Section of the Bodleian Library.

We would beat her idly about the buttocks with the red-hot mulling poker and soon she would fall into a sulky silence.

There was but one thing we knew about Mitchell Dever.

And it was this:

Every morning at seven sharp the landlord of the Jug and Arlott, the shifty-thumbed, crank-elbowed Statham, would place outside his door two cases of mentholated vodka, a jeroboam of Rae and Stollmeyer self-propelled rum, a magnum of Brown and Robertson Nursery End crusted port, seven carboys of Keating's home-made cricket bag gin and six crates of Umrigar's Fully Authorised and Harmonious India Pale Ale.

The ration was repeated at nine in the evening – plus two miniature Vimtos.

Thus might the matter have stood to take its rightful place in the history of the world's great mysteries like the disappearance of the *Marie Celeste*, the home life of the gatekeepers at Lords and the identity of the head in Chris Lewis's batting helmet.

Until one evening to our astonishment and unbounded amazement Statham dashed down the stairs three at a time, burst into the snug and cried out:

'He's just spoken to me. Through the keyhole it was. He says he wants someone to give him the last rites.'

Silence.

Total silence.

Silence as cold as the sound of laughter at a Little and Large Celebrity concert in the Long Room at Lord's.

Silence as animated as the sound of Keith Fletcher talking to his cousin's carpet slippers.

You could have heard a winter moth fart in the umpires' urinals at Worksop.

You could have heard the pound of Raymond Illingworth's heart when he first saw Ted Dexter eating pickled onions in the nude.

We stared at each other blankly.

What to do?

The village blacksmith, Gooch, rustled nervously at his bag of iron-filing-flavoured crisps.

Old Ma Botham began to pick Grannie Swanton's back teeth with her Swiss Army knife.

The village idiot, old Ben Stansgate, exposed himself to the grandmother clock.

It was time for action.

Mustering up every scrap of my reserves of reverence and solemnity I rose to my feet and said in slow and stately fashion:

'Is there a left-footer in the house?'

There was not.

The less malodorous of the Tufnell twins, who had just been awarded a badge with distinction for giving pyorrhoea to the Rover Scouts, vouchsafed that he had once been personally circumcised at the age of seven, but on taking a swift show of hands of all present it was decided by 'a narrow margin' that this did not quite fulfil the liturgical rites of the Church of Rome as practised among consenting county cricketers.

There was nothing for it – I had to do my duty.

As a man of impeccable military background and as an unashamed admirer of Italian football who had twice seen the Holy Father score a hat trick for Inter Milan on the moving television I had unrivalled qualifications for the task.

I volunteered immediately.

After a swift induction by Squire Brearley into the more esoteric canons and customs of Lollard anti-clericalism plus a brief seminar on the heresies of the Orthodox Church of Bulgaria I was ready to step forth.

The old Squire followed me to the door and whispered:

'You'll need your impediments, you know.'

I made a hasty examination of the contents of the nether regions of my popping crease and replied:

'Don't worry. They're all there.'

He shook his head.

'No,' he said. 'I mean the impediments of the last rites.'

He pressed some objects into my hand.

'I doubt if these meet the strictest demands of the Third Vatican Council, but they'll have to do. It's all I've got.'

I thanked him profusely and stepped outside.

I looked at the objects he had given me.

They consisted of half a Zippo cigarette lighter, a wad of chewing tobacco, a phial of scented wart remover, and an arrowroot biscuit covered in fluff and bootleg gentleman's relish.

And so, thus armed, I made my way upstairs, knocked on the door of the guest room and to my surprise was admitted forthwith and without demur.

Words cannot do justice to the sight which met my eyes.

Why should they have done?

In my long experience of English literature words have never done justice to anything – apart, that is, from showing unfailingly the marked similarity between the cricket reports of Mr Tony Lewis and the Government health warnings printed on packets of junior gas mask restorer.

Suffice it to say that the whole room reeked of fetid toenails, was waist deep in bottles of every size, shape and hue, and Mitchell Dever was lying on his bed wrapped tightly in brewer's underfelt and drinking Stephens light blue washable ink from a cracked saucer.

'Are you the padre?' he said.

I nodded.

'Old Father Nut and Bolt, eh?'

I nodded again.

'Well, it's no use coming to me,' he bellowed. 'I'm a bloody Methodist.'

I pondered the theological implications of this intelligence, but decided to keep my silence, having once had in the past a most unfortunate experience on Bondi beach, involving a striped deck chair, a Jesuit volley ball consultant and two Congregationalist life-savers.

Mitchell Dever sighed.

He took out his fountain pen and filled up his saucer with ink.

'Fancy a snorter?' he said.

I shook my head.

For several minutes nothing was said and then suddenly Mitchell Dever lumbered unsteadily to his feet, dragged out his Gladstone bag from under the bed, opened it, took out several volumes of thick, leather-bound scrapbooks covered in budgerigar droppings and hurled them to the floor.

'Look at that lot,' he said. 'My life's work. The product of a hard life's literary labours – bloody sports reports.'

At this he burst into tears and flung himself back onto his bed, sobbing uncontrollably.

After a while he composed himself and said:

'I'd like you to read them to me. It's not too much trouble, is it?'

I shook my head.

I opened one of the books and recoiling slightly from the ensuing blast of alcohol-friendly dust, commenced to peruse the faded yellowing, flaking cutting.

'Read it,' he pleaded. 'Read it out loud to me.'

I read out the bold-letter headline:

'MITCHELL DEVER AT THE WEMBLEY HORSE SHOW'

He sighed.

'I remember it well,' he said. 'I went there in the office horsebox. The forage was disgusting. Raymond Brooks-Ward pinched all my pony nuts.

'My God, how I detest show jumping.'

He sighed again and then he said, somewhat testily I thought:

'Well go on, you bastard, read on.'

I did.

And this is what I read out to him:

'Come with me to the white-hot cauldron of drama and excitement which is Wembley Stadium.

'Here man and beast pit their wits and their strength against the ferocious wiles and devilish intricacies of an obstacle course which would tax the skills of a great symphony orchestra playing an overture by Janáček or blanch the courage of Indian Army lancers charging into the mouths of breech-loading cannons of mustachioed, sharp-eyed, icy-toothed Afghan tribesmen from the bleak and barren plateaux and peaks of the North West Frontier.'

He held up his hand for me to stop.

I did so.

'And to think I once wanted to be the second Jane Austen,' he said.

I was about to tell him that Mr David Gower had already beaten him to it, but he motioned for me to select another cutting and read it out loud to him.

This I did.

The bold and rampant headline trumpeted out:

'MITCHELL DEVER AT HERNE HILL'

He clasped his hands to his ears and groaned most piteously.

'Cycling!' he said. 'My God, how I hate it.

'It is without doubt the most crushingly boring and tedious sport it has ever been my misfortune to witness in the whole of my life.

'What possesses grown men with half-paid endowment mortgage policies and scabs on their kneecaps to spend all day on bicycles staring into the cracks in each other's backsides is quite beyond me.

'How I hate them.'

He rummaged among the bottles nuzzling at the dado rails, selected one and drank deeply from its neck.

'Go on,' he said grumpily. 'Read what I wrote.'

This I did.

'Come with me to the white-hot cauldron of throbbing, searing, pulsating excitement which is the velodrome at Herne Hill.

'Here the modern-day gladiators play out a drama of tragedy and triumph, of exultation and despair, Greek in its proportions, Shakespearean in its passions, Chekhovian in its dark undertones of misery and gloom and Pinteresque in the terseness of its ironies and the flamboyance of its menace.

'Yes, this is the gripping and totally compelling sport of cycling.'

He supped greedily at his bottle.

A spider, stilt-legged and hump-shouldered, picked its way fastidiously over a mound of dirty socks and rotting singlets.

A mouse poked its head out of a hole in the skirting boards, sniffed disdainfully and vanished.

Mitchell Dever glanced at me slyly over the neck of the bottle and said:

'Do you remember Pirandello?'

'Yes, I rather think I do,' I said. 'Didn't he win the Tour de France in 1953?'

'No, you bastard,' he shrieked. 'He was a writer. He was a real writer. Not like me. He wrote things of value. He wrote things of beauty. Things that could be dedicated to posterity.

'Not like me. Not like poor old me.'

He took another draught from his bottle.

'See if you can find that bit I wrote on speedway,' he said. 'I was rather proud of that.'

After a while I found the relevant cutting and, on receiving a nod of approval, commenced to read it out.

It went thus:

'Come with me to the white-hot cauldron of drama and excitement which is Wembley Stadium on the night of a Test Match between those two most implacable of sporting foes, England and Australia.

'The lights dim.

'The giant stadium is hushed.

'It is the breathless pause before the opening bars of a symphony by Mahler.

'It is the silence in the eyes of the Mona Lisa.

'It is as though the Niagara Falls had stopped its primeval hurtle and tumble and the spray is frozen into eternal and expectant immobility like the echo after the last note of a Schubert Lied or the sigh of orgiastic content when you turn the last page of a novel by Flaubert.'

I looked up and saw that he had slumped back on to his pillow, his eyes closed and tiny muscles twitching at the side of his sodden gaping mouth.

I turned to tiptoe out of the room, but he called after me:

'If I hadn't had such trouble with my hamstrings, I could have been another Beryl Bainbridge.'

I nodded sympathetically.

'I think your knees might have let you down, too,' I said.

He sighed long and deeply.

'And now it's all too late,' he said. 'My life has run its course and now I am prepared for death.'

I spoke up immediately.

'Well, if that's how you feel, I think I've got some of the essential gadgets to help you on your way,' I said, fingering in my pockets the objects given to me half an hour previously by old Squire Brearley.

He did not seem to have heard me, for he continued in that mumbling monotone:

'I want to die. That's why I've been coming here to Witney Scrotum for all these years.'

'Why?' I said.

'Because it's the nearest thing to death I've ever encountered in the whole of my life.'

The cheek of it.

The downright gall.

I felt a hot flush of rage rilling up the right leg of my plus fours and was about to apprise the brute of the many and varied delights and attractions of our village, including the multi-coloured fairy lights attached to old Grannie Swanton's thermal corselettes each Christmas, the annual Festival of Bad Table Manners at the golf ball museum and our Whitsuntide Ceremony of the Blessing of Gum Boils and Athlete's Foot.

But I checked myself, for I saw a ruddy glow had appeared on the previously waxen pallor of his forehead, and his whole body seemed to be suffused with a glow of contentment and tranquillity.

'Yes,' he said. 'Now I am ready to die.'

Next morning Statham found him dead in his bed.

He summoned me and the village constable, PC 'Percy' Pocock, to examine the room.

The cadaver lay on the bed like a batch of condemned stumpers' bolsters.

And propped up on the bedside table was a large, stiff manilla envelope on which was written:

'For Father Nut and Bolt.'

I picked it up and said:

'I think this is for me.'

I opened the envelope, took out the enclosed letter and read the following:

'Come with me to the white-hot cauldron of drama and excitement which is Death.

'It is the pause before . . .

'No, it isn't.

'It's boring.

'It's boring.

'It's tedious.

'It's the icy tongue of the mournful bell tolling the homebound plod of winter-roosting gulls.

'Still, I suppose anything's better than having to watch another bloody innings by Trevor Bailey.'

CHAPTER SEVEN

The Trusty Old Lanchester

A curious melancholy filled my soul.

Torpor dogged my heels like a homesick otter.

Languor yawned in the rafters of my mind like a dormouse bored with its tail.

Ennui heaved its leaden limbs through the sodden thickets of my gloom like a sullen slug browsing on the damp lettuce of an umpire's salad.

Despite a succession of regular and highly satisfying bowel movements on the ablutions front I felt a deep sense of unease with myself.

Why should this have been?

Outwardly there was nothing to disturb my peace and equanimity.

The news from the Trucial States was consistently good.

Despite reports of an outbreak of sandbag-sniffing in Trondheim I had no reason to feel concerned about the fate of Norway.

I was informed by those 'in the know' that Peru was in excellent nick.

To my great delight Colonel 'Mad Bob' Willis had once again been chosen by the girls from the Ordnance Survey typing pool as the man with the finest unfenced elbows in Berkshire.

And here in our beloved Witney Scrotum all was well with the world.

Every enterprise prospered with scarce a trace of wallaby-baiting, mass deforestation or unprovoked hedge-trimming.

Farmer Emburey had just harvested the new season's first crop of absorbent pipe cleaners and our local branch of the Guild of Rural Wife Swappers had been most active throughout the year, thus reviving hopes that in the not too distant future Witney Scrotum would be twinned with Bangkok.

Old Grannie Swanton had recently been awarded the BEM for services to flatulence, and Statham, the landlord of the Jug and Arlott, had won for the second year in succession the English Heritage 'Thomas Hardy' prize for the most malicious urinals in the whole of Wessex.

And, most gratifying of all, the annual Festival of Speeding and Drunken Driving attracted record entries and was won once more by a senior member of the Royal Family who also came second in the Bumping Your Head on a Rubber Hot Water Bottle competition.

But wait.

Hold on, dear readers.

Driving?

Was that the source of all my woes?

Cars?

Were they the grey, slinking wolves of the night, that slavered at my joy and gnawed at the bleak bones of my content?

The briefest of brief contemplation of this notion caused my stumper's mallet to wilt of an instant in its Thermogene scabbard and my mentholated plus fours to throb uncontrollably.

I felt for all the world like Benedict on being told that Beatrice was a 'chucker'.

I felt like Romeo when he discovered that Juliet had once spent the night unaccompanied by chaperone in Curtly Ambrose's cricket bag.

I felt like Freddie Trueman when after years of lonely and intense scholarship he determined that Beethoven had not after all played second trombone for Manuel and His Music of the Mountains.

How could the driving of moving motor cars have reduced me to such a desperate and parlous state of misery?

Motor vehicles and all aspects pertaining had played a major part in my life ever since my father of late and loathsome memory had been run over by a camel transporter whilst on active service with the Royal Corps of Amateur Dermatologists in Stockton-on-Tees.

Had I not once personally sucked the gear lever of the great Carricola's Mercedes at Pau?

Had I not once during thirty-seven laps of the British Grand Prix at Silverstone sat on the lap of Miss Ann Shelton in the dicky seat of Stirling Moss's BRM?

And how to explain all those bewitching and beguiling motoring tours I had made with such leisurely grace along the highways and byways of continental Europe?

Ah, the bliss of these enchanting memories!

Ramming the Leaning Tower of Pisa in the bottle green Humber in 1927.

Demolishing the three central piers of the Roman aqueduct at Segovia in the maroon and dove grey Lea Francis in the spring of 1931.

Trapping Hilaire Belloc by the book tokens under the front mudguards of the lilac and mustard Lagonda on the road to Rome in 1933.

Were these experiences all for naught?

Yes, dear readers, they were.

Relentlessly like the trudge of dusk-bowed umpire to weary pavilion, remorselessly like the strident ring of telephone in owl-scuppered night, the truth came crashing through the fragile barriers of my dissemblance to irrigate in its sparkling waters the long-parched, weed-choked neglected pastures of my unspuriousness.

I realised in a flash that I hated motors and motoring.

Yes, my friends, I could not deny it.

Despite fifty unbroken years of motoring in my trusty navy blue Lanchester I realised that I had always basically and deep down considered myself a fully paid-up and consenting member of 'the non-driving fraternity'.

It came to me that the only reason I ever drove the car was that since the untimely death of Golden Miller I could not find a horse trustworthy enough to pull the bloody thing unsupervised.

To admit that simple fact was to unyoke myself of half a century of pretence and cynical hypocrisy.

I had, as the shirt-lifting sodality put it so succinctly, 'come out'.

I felt the freedom of soul and spirit that must have been experienced when the blessed E.R. 'Elizabeth Regina' Dexter finally felt able to admit that he was a closet Vimto addict and had always secretly envied Christopher Martin-Jenkins his hyphen.

To unburden myself of that guilt was to toss off the drab of my deception and run faun-like through meadow and glade with the simple innocence and lissom grace of Mr Fred Rumsey cavorting naked through a Heavy Duty Goods Vehicle car wash in Macclesfield.

Of course, of course.

Cars had always incensed and infuriated me.

Driving had always been a torture to me.

All those ghastly impediments that get in the way of what should be the perfectly simple task of driving from Point A to Point B.

And here I thought of those vastly over-technical devices like steering wheel, ash tray and those pedal gadgets that make the car go faster provided you remember which one to push.

How I objected, too, to those gruesome seat belts.

The bloody things had a life of their own.

Like all my acquaintances I had always found it necessary after wearing them in the car to have an operation under local anaesthetic to free myself of the wretched objects.

And as for trying to refold a road map when it was all stuck up with child repellant and gentleman's relish, well, it would defy the expertise of a Vasco da Gama or the ingenuity of a top dan in Japanese origami.

No, the whole business of driving a car was thoroughly disagreeable and best left to those simple, witless creatures whose major ambition in life is to be able to whistle the Estonian national anthem whilst standing one-legged in a vat of giraffe sick.

I thought of the previous week when I had had occasion to drive to Keating New Town to purchase emergency supplies of emery paper for the Lady Wife's shins.

I parked the trusty Lanchester in its customary place – on the pavement in front of the bus stop and blocking the main taxi rank outside the railway station.

I returned from my shopping expedition complete with emery paper, tin helmet restorer and medicated barbed wire for the toilet roll dispenser in the guest bathroom and drove off in high good spirits.

About a mile or so outside Keating New Town I was alerted to a curious violent bucking and bouncing motion of the car, which I remembered had commenced as soon as I had left my parking space outside the station.

I stopped the car and stepped out smartly to discover that I must have inadvertently run over a giant, bright orange Frisbee.

There it was clamped firmly to my front off side wheel.

I acted swiftly.

I hunted out the tool kit in the rear boot of the car, took out the two sticks of dynamite I habitually keep in case of emergency and removed the offending article by means of a small controlled explosion.

Typical, I thought, of the scum who use our modern turnpikes and cross-country arterials.

Forever littering the highway with their traffic bollards, Belisha beacons, bus shelters, telephone junction boxes and red and white plastic dunces' caps.

My policy is to ignore them completely and drive straight on.

If they cannot be bothered to look after their property, why the blitheration should I endanger life and limb by trying to avoid them when driving at high speed – sometimes in excess of twenty miles per hour when a mood of devil-may-care abandon possesses me.

I had thought I had found the ideal solution to all these difficulties when, during a visit to the United States of America in the mid-Eighties to deliver a special consignment of Teddy Tail jigsaw puzzles to the then President Regan and his beautiful consort, the ex-singing star, Joan, the Lady Wife insisted that we hire a self-drive car.

Self-drive – it seemed the answer to all my problems.

Imagine my disgust and abhorrence when I discovered that, despite the unashamed hyperbole of the advertising material, the car did not in fact drive itself.

I sat in the front driving seat for hour after hour berating the brute to behave itself and drive us forthwith to Washington DC, where, according to my 1937 edition of *Pears Encyclopaedia*, the President was wont to reside from time to time.

It was all to no avail.

The beast sat there impassively, blinking at me smugly with its battery of inflammable cigar lighters, digital binnacles and a dashboard the size of the Oval sightscreen.

At length on the somewhat tart suggestion of the Lady Wife I adjusted my bicycle clips, tightened the chinstrap of my sou'wester and commenced to drive the bloody thing myself.

I was swiftly to discover that it required a Master's degree in Advanced Applied Science to work the windscreen wipers and, when I pressed the button of the talking wireless, it did not transmit, as I had every right to expect, the BBC Test Match Special Ball by Ball commentary from Trent Bridge, but rather a singer who to my untutored ears appeared to have a dry cleaner's stapling machine attached to his sinuses and a jumbo-sized vegetarian hot dog wedged firmly up his backside.

Looking back on it I suppose it was then that the first realisation of the disenchantment I had always felt for the motor car first took root.

And it struck me as I pondered long and deep on my not unwelcome predicament that society had created a new breed of human being – one who when born did not immediately reach out puckered lips for its mother's tit, but rather stretched out its chubby hand to insert a 50p piece into a free parking meter.

There was only one thing to do.

I called on the Commodore as the evening shadows cascaded down the massive buttresses of Botham's Gut and crept waif-like through the lilting water meadows at Cowdrey's Bottom and we betook ourselves to the trusty navy blue Lanchester waiting patiently for us in my garage.

I removed three corpses of the Commodore's Rhode Island Reds from the front bumper and we drove off slowly.

'Did you remember to open the garage doors?' said the Commodore.

'I think so,' I replied.

I drove some distance beyond the confines of the village and, selecting a suitable pasture on the banks of the River Buse, I drove in, and we got out of the car.

I had no need to tell the Commodore what to do.

Silently we collected kindling wood.

Silently we stacked it round the trusty old navy blue Lanchester.

Silently we doused the pile in great draughts of the Commodore's home-made stoat-flavoured rum and set fire to it.

When the whole edifice was well ablaze and crackling fiercely we pushed it gently, almost reverently, into the yielding arms of the river and set it on its course downstream.

'That's what the wallahs in India do to their lady wives when they pass their sell-by date,' I said.

The Commodore nodded wisely.

I slapped him warmly on the back and said:

'I can't wait till the lady wife goes to the quack for her next MOT.'

With tears in our eyes and sadness seeping up through the soles of our mutual plimsolls we watched the burning car slowly disappear from view.

Next morning we were confronted by an agitated Prodger, the village poacher.

He informed us breathlessly that the carcass of the burnt-out hulk of the old Lanchester had lodged itself firmly beneath the bridge at Tremlett's Corner, thus irredeemably blocking all six lanes of the motorway.

With joy soaring and spiralling in our hearts we hurried to the site, sharing jointly the rear seat of Prodger's tandem.

What a sight met our eyes.

Prodger was right.

The motorway was at a complete standstill.

As far as the eye could see was a stationary jam of snarling, belching, snuffling, grumbling, grousing, sobbing, spluttering traffic.

You could not have asked to see a more typical cross section of the vehicles and people who currently defile and despoil the tranquil tenor of all that is best and goodly in this blessed sceptred isle of ours – lorries bearing pumice stones from Aberdeen, dolly blues and tuning forks from Wolverhampton, lamp lighters' clogs from Bolton, gravediggers' singlets and florists' spats from Dartford, chiropodists' umbrellas from Gateshead.

And more.

Oh yes, more by far.

Hatchbacks, roof-racked with racing bikes, dentists' hat stands, stone masons' wheelbarrows, and coat-hangered with commercial travellers and air attachés from the Liberian embassy.

Coupés driven by ostrich farmers, hockey coaches, designers of gardening tokens and spirit lamps, lecturers in field hygiene and the history of drawbridges, arsonists, suspended National Hunt jockeys and distant relatives of Dodie Smith.

Minibuses heaving with Moroccan contortionists, Swedish clarinettists, Latvian conjurors, stunt pilots from Ecuador and crazy golf champions from Brunei.

And on a section of the hard shoulder a party of Welsh rugby enthusiasts was earnestly and joylessly barbecuing an itinerant pigeon fancier's underpants.

We looked with the deepest affection at the remains of the trusty old Lanchester.

On its tired old twisted radiator grill was a long, slow smile of radiant happiness.

And on our tired old radiator grills there spread the identical smile.

We turned away.

Prodger had gone.

'How are we going to get back?' said the Commodore.

I groaned.

I threw up my arms and very softly I said:

'A car.

'My kingdom for a car.'

CHAPTER EIGHT

Split Runciman

There comes a time in the span of every man when he buys a new puppy and he prods idly at its pink, mottled belly with his ballpoint and he sniffs the starch-stiff whisker at the end of its incipient whatsit and for the first time in his life he thinks to himself:

My God, this little bugger could last me out.

It could easily outlive me.

I think I'll take it back and change it for a packet of chocolate digestives.

There comes a time, too, when a man muses contentedly in his fug-warm study on an ice-tingled winter's evening, when his lady wife sleeps smugly upstairs in the conjugal container, snoring like a sated barn owl, and he dribbles into his port and slurks into his pipe and thinks of his youth and says to himself:

When I was young I always fancied having an affair with an older woman.

I still do.

The trouble is all the older women I fancy now are years younger than me.

With thoughts of such profundity and elegance who needs the stimulus of outside influence to entertain and exhilarate the brain?

What price a rich juicy fart in the bath compared with a Chopin nocturne?

What price a vigorous fleck and scratching of the itching midnight crutch compared to the ghastly, withered wailings of the Beverley Sisters, Alec, Eric and Joy?

Thus it is with all of us who live in our beloved Witney Scrotum – we make do with the simple pleasures of life.

The sight of Mrs Botham trapping her massive, heaving bosoms in the swing doors of the cricket bag repository in late September is enough to keep us amused and content for the whole of the subsequent winter.

A lantern slide lecture by old Squire Brearley entitled 'A Brief History of Monasticism Among the Early Heretics of the Antioch Diaspora' is all we need for a month of sound sleep and blameless, untroubled dreams.

The so-called delights of the moving television and the electric kinograph are not for us.

We are perfectly happy to be left to our own devices and our own simple amusements.

See the flush of pleasure suffusing the innocent brow of old Grannie Swanton as she browses silly as a manatee through her priceless collection of unexploded German incendiary bombs and *fin-de-siècle* Finnish erotica.

And how blissful are the humours and tempers of the young Tufnell twins as they munch greedy as untamed Hoovers at their Semtex sandwiches after vandalising the ski lift in the mobile chiropodist's.

And is there anything to match the rapturous delight of dear Miss Roebuck from the dog biscuit shop as she wreathes round PC 'Percy' Pocock's personal truncheon gilly flowers and regurgitated corn dollies?

Yes, dear readers, here in Witney Scrotum we are most blessedly immune from the wheedling blandishments, the seductive siren songs and the tawdry baubles of the great world yonder.

There is, however, I have to state, one exception.

I refer, of course, to the annual visit of Colonel 'Mad Bob' Willis's travelling fun fair, kiddies' menagerie and semi-waterproof Big Top.

Oh, how we long for it as winter stiffens our pyjama cords and curdles the anti-freeze in the thin gruel of the village elders, begging forlornly for alms outside the local branch of the MCC Sock Shop.

Oh, how we crave for it as spring whispers shyly through the breasts of young lovers locked in their passionate embraces in abandoned antenatal clinics in the water meadows at Cowdrey's Bottom and wickedly rouses old Ben Stansgate to apply fresh dubbin to the hem of his flasher's raincoat.

Oh, how we 'hurrah' and hurl our hats into the air as the cavalcade wheels into our village on that day sacred to the ecclesiastical calendar – the First Sunday After The Lord's Test.

This year was no different.

First came the elephants with the Mahatma Boycott perched high on the leading beast, doffing his panama and throwing blank cheques, second-hand diphthongs and poisoned liquorice bootlaces to the thronging children.

Then came the tumblers and the clowns setting light to each other's jockstraps, sucking their arch supports and stuffing their underpants with greengages for all the world like English middle order batsmen on 'a good day' in the West Indies.

The chaste young village maidens flocked round the strongman, The Mighty Higgs, who flexed his biceps and flashed his benefit brochure most fearsomely, causing Miss Roebuck to fall into a dead swoon in the path of Mr Fred Dibner's mobile filter-tipped chimney stack.

When we dragged her clear and revived her with stirrup pump and Dynarod, we found she was covered from head to foot in zebra dung and the saliva of performing sealions and unicycling giraffes.

'Not to worry,' she said after she had recovered. 'I've been through far worse at a Nat West cup tie on the county ground at Taunton.'

Later, in the company of the Lady Wife and the Commodore, I pottered happily round the compound of the kiddies' menagerie.

What joy.

We admired the man-eating hamsters, marvelled at the giant gerbils and fed the miniature polar bears with our leatherette pension book holders.

We spat at the llamas, made mutual rude gestures at the baboons, and threw cream soda over each other at the chimps' tea party.

The only disappointment was that once again the Siberian wolf showed a marked and cowardly reluctance to savage the Lady Wife.

And thus did the night draw its star-spangled coverlet over the village, snuggling it in the scents of hot dog and candy floss, lulling it with the wheezing yarl of steam engine, the sinewy hiss of hurricane lamp and the cries of small children abandoned by their parents at the top of the Ferris wheel.

Yes, the fun fair had commenced.

And what fun the Commodore and I had on the dodgems as we rammed the Lady Wife, battered her, biffed her, bashed her, caused her eyeballs to pop out of their sockets and her teeth to rattle like Sten guns.

'Why didn't you tell me I had to get into one of the cars?' she said as she limped away from the booth.

We went on the waltzers and of an instant the Commodore was violently sick.

'I thought you said you were used to rough seas,' snarled the Lady Wife.

'I am,' said the Commodore. 'It's just that I'm not used to being in such close proximity to you.'

We visited the hoopla stall where Oslear, the honorary toad circumciser, managed most deftly to throw three successive rubber rings round the Lady Wife's neck.

He claimed he was aiming at the goldfish in a plastic bag and was thus 'let off'.

We moved to the boxing booth and watched the battered, puff-eyed, flat-nosed, chew-eared pugilists as they slouched on parade, scratching their private parts with lavatory brushes and probing in their ears with bent car aerials.

'Isn't that one with the ingratiating teeth Martin Jarvis?' said the Lady Wife.

Eventually we went inside the booth and the Lady Wife won a year's free supplies of gum shields when she soundly thrashed the former cruiserweight champion of the Dutch East Indies.

'Is she by any chance related to Rocky Marciano?' the proprietor asked me.

'I don't know,' I replied. 'I've never been that intimate with her.'

On the shooting range the Lady Wife achieved outstanding success.

She severely 'winged' in the left baldachin our chaste, gum-grinned, rose-blushed young curate, the Rev. Michael Atherton, recently arrived with a fine record of pastoral duties among dissident gondola salesmen on the Manchester Ship Canal.

She shot the medicated loofah out of the dithering hands of the village odd-job man, Fletcher, as he lay in his bath, playing with his inflatable colouring books and trying to work out how to operate his shaving mirror.

She put out all the fairy lights on the St John's Ambulance horse-drawn boy scouts' rest room.

Only after the most vicious of struggles with a detachment of SAS shock troops who were most fortuitously passing en route to guard duties at the Chichester Festival was she finally disarmed and we were able to make our way to the Wall of Death.

I confess I did not stay long enough to witness the Lady Wife riding no-handed and backwards the stripped-down Rudge autocycle with old Squire Brearley strapped to her broad shoulders placidly reciting previously unknown verses of Plutarch which he had discovered lurking in Mr Merv Kitchen's umpires' vanitory case.

I was tired.

I was exhausted.

I slipped away in the coolsome darkness, slumped to the welcome of the soft, springy turf and was just about to take a long and hearty swig from the bottle of home-made corn plaster gin I had secreted in the false bottom of my plus fours, when I saw a shadowy figure dart out from a small door in the side of the Wall of Death.

It was dressed in scuffed, creaking, black leathers encrusted in dromedary snot.

Its shoulders were hunched.

Its back was bowed.

Its legs were bandy and its feet were splayed.

But even behind the Royal Flying Corps goggles and the crash helmet the size of a Fylingdales early-warning sphere I recognised it instantly.

'Split' Runciman.

'Split' Runciman, the erstwhile colossus of the speedway track.

'Split' Runciman, whose performance on the cinders had kept me sane during the long and ghastly drag of my enforced sojourn in London all those years ago during the war when I was on detachment as searchlight adviser to the Ministry of Cakes.

During that period of utter wretchedness and unbearable misery I had tried everything to keep my despair at bay.

I had lingered expectantly in front of the pictures at the National Portrait Gallery, but I didn't recognise any of the faces.

I had gone to musical symphony concerts at the Royal Albert Hall, but I couldn't stand the smell of the trombonists' armpits.

I had taken afternoon tea at the Ritz and dined at the Savoy Grill, but discovered I didn't like eating rissoles in public.

No, it was only my regular visits to New Cross Stadium to see dear old 'Split' Runciman scorching round the track that had kept me sane and prevented my flinging myself bodily under the front wheels of a Woolwich trolley bus.

I would have preferred the Catford-bound vehicle, but it wasn't on my route home.

I banished these memories and hoisted myself to my feet and followed the leather-clad figure through the lurking shadows.

It paused before a battered caravan with an arthritic bent stovepipe chimney and hoof marks on its deeply dented sides.

It looked furtively over its shoulder and then slipped inside.

A faint green flickering light appeared at the scowling window.

And presently came the distinctive smell of frying gauntlets.

I took my courage into both of my respective hands and tapped softly on the cockeyed door.

It was opened instantly.

A clawed, horny, prehensile hand grabbed me roughly by the scruff of the neck, dragged me inside and hurled me to the floor.

I looked up.

Two eyes the colour and size of condemned weasel tods glared at me beadily.

Pale, thin lips the texture and consistency of the rim of a pole vaulter's rubber hot water bottle twitched silently.

He stared at me silently for a while and then quite suddenly his face creased into a toothless grin that would have stopped a rampant cream cracker dead in its tracks.

He offered me his hands, pulled me to my feet and dusted me down diligently and tenderly with his archivist's Ewbank.

Then he smiled again and said:

'I know who you are.'

'Do you?' I said.

'Yes,' he said. 'You're the old lady who used to run the temperance heel bar at Belle Vue speedway.'

I should have liked to have confirmed his conclusion regarding my identity, but in all honesty I could not do so, owing to my obvious lack of female appendages and my even more obvious lack of knowledge of the cobbler's art.

I, therefore, revealed my true identity.

To my amazement he greeted this intelligence with every sign of equanimity.

When I further told him of my profound affection towards him and the efficacious effect he had had on my mood of deepest melancholy during my importunate exile in the brumous, gas-masked vaporosity of war-time London his mien became positively perky and chirpy.

And after quaffing liberal quantities of my home-made tyre lever brandy, he became gushingly loquacious.

Thus it was that he recounted to me the history of his distinguished career.

He told me that it had started in the dim and distant past when as a boy in Swindon his mother had bought him a speedway bike in the hope that it would stop him stealing carrots and reading secretly the works of Colette and R.C. Robertson-Glasgow.

'That machine – he was a brute and no mistake,' said 'Split' in those familiar, rolling, burring vowels of Wiltshire that cherish the soul and nurture the spirit like the noble, soaring tones of our beloved Dame Barbara Dixon when she's singing with her voice in public.

He continued:

'I remember riding him full throttle, bucking and bouncing on him, great choking clouds of cinders and clinkers spraying and splattering all over.'

'And that was in the loam-red fields of Wiltshire, I suppose?' I said.

'No,' he said. 'That was in our mum's front parlour.'

He smiled warmly and his voice mellowed as he said:

'Our mum says to me: "If you're going to behave like that, leaving skid marks all over the lino and buggering up the bottom of the parrot's cage, you'd better start doing it professional." '

And this he did.

Such was his natural talent that in next to no time he had joined New Cross, won the Golden Helmet outright, represented his country at Test Match level on twenty-five successive occasions and been invited to share a golfing holiday with Princess Alice of Athlone and the Western Brothers, Kenneth and George.

'It was shortly after that I married my first wife with the big tits,' he said.

I nodded wisely.

I should have done exactly the same had he informed me in similar manner that he had once lost a cough lozenge in Wolverhampton.

And then I said I had reason to believe that he had called himself 'Split' Runciman in honour of the famous speedway star, 'Split' Waterman.

'Oh no,' he said. 'I called myself "Split" Runciman after the famous historian, Sir Steven Runciman, what wrote all them books about the Crusaders.

'I don't think he ever rode National League speedway for Cradley Heath, but, by God, he didn't half know his onions as regards the bleeding Mamelukes.'

It was whilst attending a course in tea-straining for beginners at the Horniman Museum that he 'saw the light'.

It was in one of those blinding flashes of insight and inspiration that have so often in the past irreversibly changed the course of the history of mankind that he transferred his attentions from speedway and took up scrambling and motocross.

He bought himself a Swedish bike, the name of which he could not quite pronounce, and soon he was practising every minute of the day on the snarling machine, plunging and plummeting like a crazed wild bronco, howling and screeching and hurtling recklessly at full throttle, gritting his teeth and clinging like grim death to the handlebars.

'I suppose that was in the nightingaled woodlands of deepest Wiltshire?' I said.

'Oh no,' he said. 'That was up and down the stairs of the maisonette in Erith I bought my second wife with the fat arse.'

And thus was born the sport of indoor motor cycling.

'Split' Runciman proved himself a genuine 'natural'.

He won the first indoor scramble round Buckingham Palace even though on the third lap he got his clutch lever stuck in the nozzle of Princess Margaret's self-filling hip flask.

He would have won the event a record six times had it not been for Prince Philip misdirecting him and thus causing him to burst in on a state banquet given in honour of the president of Upper Volta, who at that time happened to be Mr Raymond Illingworth.

He did have his consolations, though.

He won the House of Commons Classic nine times and was the first winner of the twenty-lap race round the interior of Dame Flora Robson's bedroom.

He won events at the Sistine Chapel, the Bodleian Library, the Pyramids at Giza, the tram sheds at Knossos and was narrowly pipped by Mother Cliff Richard in a 'thriller' round the inside of Doctor Billy Graham's collecting box.

'But then came tragedy,' he said.

'Did it, by Jove?' I said, handing him the last of my home-made coal scuttle whisky, which he drained back in a single gulp.

'Yes indeed,' he said. 'Indeed it did.

'Well, I'd taken a bit of a tumble in the Rijksmuseum in Amsterdam and ripped three and a half yards out of *The Night Watch* by Rembrandt with my left elbow.

'I don't know what they made all the fuss about. They could have claimed it on their insurance, easy, like what I done when the ceiling fell in on my sixth wife with the big hooter when she was having a crap in our bungalow in Chislehurst.'

I nodded wisely.

I should have done exactly the same had he informed me in similar manner that he had once found a Peruvian matelot's pencil sharpener in Dunstable.

He continued.

'But the real disaster was yet to come,' he said.

'It was the first ever race round the inside of Lenin's Tomb.

'I was leading by miles. Three quarters of an hour at the very least.

'Well then, I sees this blokie lying on his back in a low-sided bed sort of thing with his hands crossed on top of his chest.

'So I gets off my bike and I says: "Budge up mate. I'll have a bit of a kip with you till the others catches me up."

'Well, that turned out to be a mortal sin and no mistake about it.'

'Of course it was,' I said. 'It was Lenin you were lying next to.'

'No it weren't,' he said. 'It were Murray Walker, weren't it?'

He smiled and then he said:

'They banned me *sine die* there and then and said in addition they'd confiscate my puncture outfit and put a moratorium on my pannier bags.'

Once more he smiled.

'Still, I'm not complaining,' he said. 'I've had a happy life and now I'm living all quiet and contented with my eighth wife with the hairy legs and the high-pitched voice.

'Oh yes, we're as happy as two wasps in a vat of cider, Murray and me.'

I bade him a fond farewell and returned late in the evening to my home.

I went upstairs to the bedroom.

The Lady Wife was lying on her back sound asleep in the conjugal container, her hands crossed across her chest.

I looked at her for a moment and then I said softly to myself:

'Do you know, on the whole I think I'd rather have Lenin.'

CHAPTER NINE

Alternative Cricket

My emotions are mixed, dear readers.

They rage. They fume.

They soar to the delights of rapture experienced by Mr Philip Tufnell when at long last on a Saturday afternoon he finally finishes reading the front page of Monday's *Sun* newspaper.

And why?

Well, I am thrilled and delighted to record in readable print the outstanding success of the first world tournament for 'Alternative Cricketers'.

Yes, the Air Wick Cup lived up to all our expectations, despite constant mild outbreaks of swooning and shrill giggling in the nefarious regions of long leg and a most unsavoury incident when the Onanists' Select XI from the United Arab Emirates were eliminated in their match against Eleven 'So-Called' Gentlemen of Marrakesh for defacing a David Hockney self-portrait of our much-lamented and revered Cec Pepper, erstwhile patron saint of crooked little fingers.

Barely have I seen waterproof lipstick and Boy Scouts' woggles used to such devastating effect.

Aggers, who for some obscure reason was known to one and all at the tournament as 'Elsie', was absolutely livid.

He got his grandmother's luminous spats into the most fearful twist and vowed 'in no uncertain terms' that never again would he pick his nose with Mr Bill Frindall's indelible pencil.

All that could I endure.

I could have tolerated and even at times condoned Mr Norman Gifford's nude sunbathing on his personal, portable slip cradle.

I was even prepared to 'turn a blind eye' to the grumpy behaviour of Mr E.W. 'Gloria' Swanton, who had been inveigled into giving his patronage to the tournament under the impression that it was the annual general meeting of the West Sussex Hamster and Edible Dormouse Fancy.

But what stuck in my gullet and gave me such yearning pain was the fact that the trophy was not won by 'our boys'.

The Gropers, a team of out-of-work dressers from the National Theatre and freelance stumpers from Northamptonshire, was soundly thrashed and deeply humiliated in the final by the Shirt Lifters, a collection of American vilenesses with false sun tans, painted toenails and only a minimal knowledge of the LBW laws relating to leg spinners bowling 'round the wicket'.

The Gropers seemed positively to revel in their debasement.

Never shall I forget their whoops of delight after the match when they plunged headfirst with their erstwhile opponents into a vat of strawberry milk shake and made the most vulgar of gestures towards the saintly Mr Raymond Illingworth, who was present in his capacity as deputy physio to the Testicle and County Cricket Board.

Whilst I have no intrinsic objection to his being constantly boarded by crew members of Royal Navy Fishery protection vessels for selecting 'off limits' I do take exception to his being constantly bombarded by quarter-scale effigies of Mr Donald Trelford.

What was I doing at the tournament?

You may well ask, dear readers.

The answer is simple.

Poor Miss Roebuck from the dog biscuit shop at our beloved Witney Scrotum had had the good fortune to win first prize in a competition sponsored by the makers of 'Nurse Gooch's Invalid Junket'.

She had had to list in order of merit the prime six virtues of Mr Colin Dredge, and on having listed 1,879 of the same was handcuffed to the golf ball museum heavy roller and awarded first prize, which was none other than an all-expenses-paid trip to the Air Wick Cup tournament.

Plus companion.

'Plus companion!'

Oh, what words of doom for poor Miss Roebuck.

Never before in the whole of her life had she had so much of 'a sniff' at a companion.

Once she had almost spoken to Mr Ian Botham.

And it is true she had once asked Mr Merv Kitchen if she might carry his snakeskin manicure case.

But as for permanent relationships with a sensate human being with skid-marked underpants and gravy-stained thermal singlets – nothing.

Thus it was that she invited me to accompany her on her 'great adventure' to Key West, where the tournament was to be held.

Key West, as I discovered from exhaustive and laborious perusal of the world atlas (including maps) the Lady Wife had won at school for her prowess at Meccano and indoor spelling Bees, was at the tip of a string of islands extending from the Florida coast to the nearest confines of Cuba, which is presently ruled by a creature purporting to be the reincarnation of Dr W.G. Grace.

I was pleased 'beyond measure' to accept her kind invitation.

The Lady Wife's odious Bedlington terriers were due for their annual castration and there were intimations of an impending visitation from her unmarried spinster sister from Cheltenham with her overpowering smell of stale acorns and condemned jam sandwiches.

Thus we set off from the aerodrome at Heathrow constantly hectored, bossed and bullied during the flight by British Airways hostesses, who to a man had all the charm and grace of a drunken charlady from the Isle of Dogs.

On the journey in the hire car from Miami Airport to Key West Miss Roebuck was mugged seven times and held up at gunpoint on six occasions.

She expressed herself well satisfied with the experience, complaining only that the cheroot-chewing dago arsonist who had set fire to her knickers two miles west of Key Largo had mistaken her for Mr Robin 'Gustav' Marlar.

We were quartered at Key West in the Ernest Hemingway house.

Mr Hemingway, I was to discover later, was an author of some repute who had written the definitive autobiography of Mr Alec Stewart, entitled *The Sun Also Rises*.

Miss Roebuck – who herself has certain literary pretensions – was entranced.

'I've met this famous writer,' she said.

'Is there such a creature?' I asked.

'Oh yes,' she said. 'He's called Tennessee Williams. Or is it Mississippi Gimblett? Anyway, he says he's written all these plays and one of them called *Cat On a Hot Tin Helmet* starred Miss Bob "Elizabeth" Taylor of Derbyshire and England.'

I said I rather thought I'd heard of him.

'Didn't he once write "Knott's Landing"?' I asked, but she just sniffed and immersed herself in her tea towel embroidery set.

Of the subsequent competition I have little memory.

I remember Oscar Wilde scoring a ton before lunch and Jean Cocteau bowling a devilish eight-over spell of googlies, flippers and Chinamen dressed in nothing but ankle-length Glamorgan sweaters and Wilf Wooller autograph sweat bands.

And of the final – nothing.

As the lugubrious Innersole said to me as we trudged away from the ground after the defeat of The Gropers:

'It's all Greek, mate, ain't it?'

'You play football for Walthamstow Avenue once and there ain't no human perversion can ever turn your head again.'

I am not inclined to agree – remember, dear readers, I once went on a bicycling holiday in the Yorkshire Dales in the company of Mr Noël Coward and Mr Bill Alley.

CHAPTER TEN

What-Ho, Vileness

I have said before that I have little fondness for letter writing.

I have a slight allergy to green blotting paper.

Nibs set my teeth on edge.

And the smell of light blue washable ink brings me out in unsightly pustules on my spectacle case.

However, there are occasions when duty compels me to put pen to paper.

Here I think particularly of the time when I was serving King and country in 'foreign' climes and was compelled to send a missive to the Lady Wife, instructing her to send urgent supplies of giraffe repellant and informing her that despite an attack of trench foot she was constantly in my thoughts.

Amazing how a chap can write legibly with his fingers crossed, isn't it?

Duty also compels me from time to time to dispatch epistles to that emaciated vileness, Tinniswood, when he is 'down in the dumps' and suffering from that deep melancholy endemic among all those poor souls who yearn for the return of the Golden Age of Stainless Stephen, Ken Cranston and Troise and his Mandoliers.

I present to you, dear readers, without comment two of my most recent billets doux.

LETTER NUMBER ONE:

What-ho, vileness.

Greetings from Witney Scrotum.

I am proud to say that I have just achieved the ultimate for all those insomniacs who habitually play three-card brag with their digital alarm clocks.

Yes, my friend, in the early hours of this morning I got three threes.

The circumstances were thus:

The Lady Wife's loathsome Bedlington terriers woke me up, trying to bury the duvet cover in their mistress's trouser press, thus sending my autographed photo of James Langridge crashing into the bedroom Aga and causing my carpet slippers to bolt for cover under the bronze Bauhaus statuette of Courtney Walsh.

I awoke with a start, grunted, vigorously scratched at the crutch of my new waterproof hill-walker's pyjamas, glanced at the alarm clock and, joy of joys, there it was in red, flickering, glowing numbers.

Three lovely pristine threes.

Three thirty-three in the morning.

I followed it up immediately with a good run of three, four and five at a quarter to four and managed to stay awake long enough for a lively if modest pair of fives at three fifty-five.

You will be surprised to learn that I love my digital alarm clock.

What a friend it has been during these long, lonely, dog hours before dawn when the starlings scutter sleepily in the eaves, the foxes howl and shriek at the bottom of the garden, the Lady Wife lies on her back, snoring like an ancient dredger wallowing in silt on a mist-shrouded Flemish estuary and I lie awake worrying myself sick about Graeme Hick.

I seem to worry about everyone these days, vileness. Why do we never see Pluto cartoons on our moving television?

Is there life as we know it in British Telecom?

If Typhoo put the T in Britain, who put the SMOG in Lord Rees-Mogg?

The digital alarm clock soothes me and cossets me in my wakefulness.

'Come on, old chap,' it says. 'You can do it.

'Only half an hour to go till five to six and you'll get three lovely fives. Give it an hour more and I'll switch on the radio automatically and you'll get Rabbi Lionel Blue on "Thought for Today".'

I can hear him now.

'Good morning, Sue. Good morning, Jim. Good morning, John. Good morning, Peter. Good morning, too, to the lift attendant who brought me up to the studio. Good morning to the lady from the canteen who fetched me my tea in a plastic beaker. Good morning to the leader of the London Symphony Orchestra and the youth coach at Millwall Football Club.

'Well, there I was in my glad rags all matey and chummy, sitting on this topless beach at Antibes with this old codger from the Mile End Road, comparing recipes for gefuellter singlets when all of a sudden . . . '

Zzzzzz.

Instant slumber.

But at the dead of night, vileness, my worries drag on and on and on.

The digital alarm clock smiles at me benignly as I toss and turn and make up quiz questions.

If you cross a singer from the Southern states of America with a natural feature of Norway, what do you get?

Answer.

Tennessee Ernie Fiord.

Zzzzzz.

I sometimes think I should have been an egg timer.

Imagine the bliss of that existence – being turned upside down every five minutes and spilling sand into your underpants.

I'd have made a wonderful vacuum cleaner, if only I'd kept my castors in good nick.

I could have been the River Ouse, if only I hadn't had such small tributaries.

The digital alarm clock puckers its lips at my fancies and my foibles.

Why aren't I a digital alarm clock?

If I were, I'm damned if I'd let myself sleep in until I got such a rotten hand of brag at nine thirty-five.

I must close now.

I have to dash to see Martin Jarvis on 'Countdown'.

LETTER NUMBER TWO:

What-ho, vileness.

Greetings from Witney Scrotum.

I am pleased to report that all is well with the world.

The dog biscuit shop has just received a new consignment of pet Colorado beetles, and migrant tram conductors and dolly blue tasters cower forlorn and shivering on the ice-chapped water meadows at Cowdrey's Bottom.

Farmer Emburey has successfully reared yet another brood of his pedigree champion savoury doorstops and the lads from the auxiliary fire brigade have at last completed the annual relagging of Grannie Swanton's thermal underskirt.

But the best news of all is that Hardcastle has now established himself in permanent residence in the village.

Through the good offices of Don 'Sir Oswald' Mosey and his Junior Blackshirts he has been comfortably quartered in the abandoned munition dump at the rear of the golf ball museum.

Who is this Hardcastle chappie, I hear you pipe in your weedy, thin-crutched, King's-singer treble.

Well, my dear vileness, let me tell that you that Hardcastle has achieved immortality (assuming it lasts that long under the present government) as Britain's most boring sportsman – thus succeeding the unbroken seven-decade reign of Mr Keith Fletcher.

What are the facts about him?

Well, he claims to be the world's first Test Tube baby owing to the fact that at the time of his conception his parents were travelling on the London Underground en route to see England play Australia at the Oval.

Of his early years little is known, although rumour has it that at the age of 12 he was South Huntingdonshire Junior Champion of Indoor Sock-sniffing and at the age of 15 was the first man to climb the inside of Mr Ian Chappell's trousers without the aid of oxygen.

He first came to my attention when he ate my father's umbrella.

This was in Burma during the infamous war of Sightscreen Desecration, and my father had arranged as a diversion from military duties an entertainment for the native scorebox wallahs and their concubines.

This was in the form of the world's first Eating an Inedible Object competition.

Hardcastle, a lance corporal in the Fifteenth Light Mounted Usherettes won 'hands down'.

Among the objects consumed during his winning streak were half a dozen ebony shoehorns, seventeen scorecard printing presses and the entire contents of Miss Delia Smith's luncheon hamper.

There was no looking back.

Honour followed upon honour.

His success knew no bounds.

Within a short space of time he had been appointed chief coach to the Ceylon national cribbage squad, won three years in succession the gravy-walking marathon from Selby to Pontefract and was undefeated World Lightweight Champion at Denture-Clicking and Freelance Grouting.

In my opinion, however, he achieved the pinnacle of his success in the 1935 Instant Possum Games at Rotherham when he won the gold medal for Grumbling with the immortal line:

'Ants eggs aren't what they used to be.'

Dear old Hardcastle, age has not withered his abilities nor shrunk the tail of his flannelette shirt.

There he sits outside his munition dump, grumbling and boring the villagers to terminal torpor with his exciting tales of buying a carpet beater in Wrexham, helping an old lady across the road in Samarkand, finding Daventry on the dial of his talking wireless, sharing a peach with Mr Laurie Fishlock of Surrey and England, buying a senior citizen's bus pass in Nantwich, witnessing the massacre of eight thousand innocent women and children at . . .

Blast.

I seem to have locked myself out of my cricket bag.

CHAPTER ELEVEN

Beryl

Sounds of a summer night.

Moth whirr. Bat squeak. Snuffle of hedgehog. Sigh of lonely singlet on soughing clothes line.

I was banished to the garden.

The Lady Wife had visitors.

Sometimes I think the Lady Wife regards me as a visitor in her life.

She has that look in her eyes when we plod solemnly up the slyly muttering stairs at the end of the day and prepare ourselves for the long and listless sojourn in the conjugal container which seems to say:

'I wish he had a home to go to.'

Sounds of a summer night.

Distant bay of lovelorn dog. Yowl of stiff-legged, arched-backed cat. The deer lap softly at the dew.

The Lady Wife had visitors: to wit, her unmarried, spinster sister from Cheltenham and her chum and companion, Beryl.

Beryl!

Ghastly name, Beryl.

It reminded me of syrup cloying in a rusty tin.

It reminded me of sullen summer storms and friendless winter carpets.

It reminded me of the gasp of stale fetid heat released when you peel off your pads after a long day's opening partnership of 13 with Michael Atherton.

Beryl was as small as a jockey's tooth.

Sights of a summer night.

Melon moon. Pears hanging heavy and plump. Sky as dark as damson jam.

Upon what did those stars look down?

Insomniac dental technicians?

Restless stallions mared with the night?

Autocycle enthusiasts with sad chins? Cookery consultants dreaming of yeast? The headstones of long-forgotten designers of stapling machines?

I repaired inside to the house.

The Lady Wife looked up from her fretwork machine and said:

'The girls have gone to bed.'

'Ah,' I said. 'Ah.'

I lit my pipe.

'Must you?' said the Lady Wife.

I doused my pipe.

The clock chimed resentfully. The loathsome Bedlington terriers twitched in their malodorous sleep.

Presently the Lady Wife put away her bradawl, furled her Bowie knife, stood up and said:

'Well then, it's me for Bedfordshire.'

'Ah,' I said. 'Ah.'

At the door she paused, flashed her piggy little eyes and said:

'I rather think Beryl's taken a shine to you.'

She left the room.

I lit my pipe.

In the gentle soothe of its swirling smoke I let my memories wander.

To whom had I taken a shine in my life?

Bert Sutcliffe?

Ah yes. Ah yes.

H.D.G. Leveson-Gower?

But of course. Of course.

Douglas Fairbanks Junior?

Ah, my friends, that is quite another story.

Next morning over a deeply reluctant breakfast the Lady Wife said to me:

'My sister and I are going out for the day. She has to see her solicitor about her out-houses. You will have to entertain Beryl.'

'Ah,' I said. 'Ah.'

I watched them leave in the unmarried spinster sister's semi-invalid Hillman Imp.

I turned and saw Beryl standing in the hall, puckering her lips and wobbling her Adam's apple.

'Would you like to kiss me?' she said.

'No thank you,' I replied. 'I've just cut my toenails.'

I beat a hasty retreat next door to the Commodore's summer house.

There was a note pinned to the door.

It said:

'Out. Gone to Peterborough.'

What was the significance of those doom-laden words?

Had he been savaged by his canary?

Had he discovered chub breeding in his header tank?

Had he been summoned urgently to that ancient Fenland city to comfort an aged cousin tragically attacked by a drink-crazed female lady bus conductress in the splendid Norman nave of that noble sky-soaring cathedral?

Had he mislaid the level crossing on his Hornby train set?

He must indeed have been in the most desperate of straits to have penned such a note.

Heavy with foreboding and sodden with misery, I returned to my house.

Beryl was sitting in an I Zingari deck chair outside the kitchen door with the implacable look of a badger guarding its sett or a gatekeeper at Lords defending his sentry box against Sunil Gavaskar.

'Excuse me,' I said. 'I have an urgent call on the ablutions front.'

'That can wait,' she said. 'Sit down.'

I looked round vainly for a receptacle in which to place my nether regions.

'You don't need a chair,' she said. 'You can sit on the ground at my feet.

'I like men to sit at my feet.'

I sat down.

At her feet.

They were small feet.

You could have used them as bookmarks for a pocket almanac of tide tables.

'Tell me about your affairs,' she said.

'They are all in order,' I said.

'Really?' she said.

'Yes,' I replied. 'I have a comfortable high yield deposit account with the Congleton and Lyme Regis Building Society and . . .'

'I'm not talking about those sort of affairs,' she snapped testily. 'I'm talking about your affairs with women.'

'Ah,' I said. 'Ah.'

She placed her hand on my knee and commenced to stroke it softly.

In such a manner did my dear mother attempt to remove the warts from my elbows when I was a small boy and the summers were as sweet as tangerines and the winters as cold as a dead adder's breath.

'Tell me,' she said. 'Have you ever looked at a woman other than your wife?'

'I don't think so,' I said. 'You all look the same to me.'

She put her hand on my thigh and I felt my latch keys twitch and my smoker's compendium whimper.

'Look at me,' she said suddenly. 'Look at me.'

I did so.

'What do you see?' she said throatily. 'Tell me what you see.'

I was about to tell her that she bore a marked resemblance to an aged Tunisian tumbler I had once seen doing cumbersome back somersaults during the half-time interval in the match which had sometimes involved the respective players of Plymouth Argyle and Charlton Athletic, when she interrupted me and said:

'Would you like to see me naked?'

'No thank you,' I said. 'I'm halfway through a course of antibiotics.'

She sighed deeply and shook her head.

'It's forever thus,' she said. 'Forever and forever thus.'

I excused myself and repaired to the drawing room.

There I lit a much-loved, second-hand Burmese cheroot and barricaded the door with, among other objects, the complete large-print edition of the collected works of Charles and Allan Lamb, my antique Gunn and Moore greyhound trainer's tallboy and the set of armoured linen baskets presented to me by my brother officers when I left the Third Battalion of the King's Own Amphibious Camel Corps after a tour of duty in the West Indies, guarding the grapefruit crop against marauding bands of Hungarian marines.

Gravely I contemplated my lot.

What to do?

I had, of course, been in 'sticky situations' before.

Danger was no stranger to me.

Had I not once single-handedly arrested the manageress of a Thornton's sweet shop for doctoring the treacle toffee?

Had I not once personally dealt with a drunken Irish dining car attendant who was attempting to stuff the ticket collector's socks with Paxo on the night mail to Fishguard?

Had I not once watched an entire programme on the moving television involving Miss Esther Rantzen and a trio of singing Rhodesian ridgebacks?

But how to cope with a woman of the opposite gender who wished to take off her togs and expose to me her doodahs in person?

Good God, she might even have hair of a vaguely pubic nature.

And what if she had flaky shins?

What to do? Oh hell, what to do?

It was possible, of course, to commit ritual suicide but I knew the Lady Wife would play gyp if she discovered I had neglected to pay the milkman.

I could always rip up the floorboards and commence to burrow a tunnel to the snug bar of the Jug and Arlott.

But what if it were closed when I broke surface?

I was damned if I was going to burrow a sub-tunnel to the front door and stand outside with old Grannie Swanton and the other village drunks till opening time arrived.

There was a knock on the door.

I stiffened every muscle and sinew.

'Who's that?' I croaked.

'It's me,' said a timid little voice.

It was Beryl's voice.

It festered round my neck like incipient shaving rash.

'What do you want?' I said hoarsely.

'I want to come in,' she said.

I grabbed the toasting fork and took up station in the left-hand cupboard of the Welsh dresser.

'Please let me in,' she said. 'I won't harm you. I won't interfere with you. Please, please let me in. I'm so lonely. I'm so miserable.'

In such tones long, long ago had my batman once pleaded with me when asking for weekend leave to attend a lunchtime concert given by Dame Myra Hess and 'Jersey Joe' Walcott in the Thomas à Becket gym down the Old Kent Road.

And now, as I did then, I succumbed to those blandishments.

My heart melted and I relented.

But before removing the barricade I took the precaution of padlocking a jumbo-sized bulldog clip to the front of my flies and binding my shirt tails firmly round my crutch with a length of non-edible fuse wire.

I opened the door.

Instantly Beryl plunged inside, struck me violently on the chest with the flat of her hand and propelled me backwards on to the chesterfield sofa.

'Sit down,' she barked. 'Shut up and listen to what I have to say.'

I cowered in the musty depths of the sofa, fearing the worst.

Oh yes, I was well versed in the horrific tales of the atrocities committed by Afghan tribesmen on their unfortunate prisoners.

God knows how many of the poor wretches had been driven to gibbering madness, compelled to read the cricket reports of Mr Tony Lewis and listen to endless repeats of 'Does He Take Sugar'.

Oh yes, I knew full well the fate of redundant Yorkshire coal miners caught eating fish and chips out of Sir Geoffrey Boycott's panama.

And so, like Chris Lewis batting in the West Indies, I shut my eyes and thought vaguely of England.

For some moments Beryl stalked silently round the room sniffing the skirting boards and glowering at the piano stool.

Then of a sudden she turned to me and said:

'I know why I never get a man. I'm too nice, aren't I? Men don't like nice women, do they? Men like women who hector and bully. Men like women who talk ceaselessly and brook no interruption.'

I opened my mouth to speak.

'Silence,' she thundered.

I closed my mouth.

The clock commenced to chime but then thought better of it.

The house spider, stilty-legged, scuttled soundlessly across the grate and squeezed itself deftly into a crack in the fender.

Beryl stared at me intently like Mr H.D. 'Dickie' Bird perusing the obituary columns of the *Beano*, and then she said in measured tones:

'My name is Beryl Stoppard.

'I am a friend of your sister-in-law.

'We share a mutual interest in lock-keeping and public executions.'

I was about to attempt to ease a ruck in my spats when she bellowed:

'Sit still.

'Stop playing with that bulldog clip.

'You never see Roman Catholics playing with bulldog clips, do you?'

After a moment's silent contemplation on matters theological, I was bound to admit to myself that never in my life had I seen members of the left-footer fraternity indulging in such activities.

Beryl continued:

'As I was saying, my name is Beryl Stoppard.

'I am a distant relative of the celebrated playwright of the same name – Alan Ayckbourn I think they call him.

'However that is as may be.

'My main claim to fame is that I have recently won first prize in my second cousin's women's magazine.

'I have been voted England's Number One lady sports fan.

'She lives in Droitwich Spa.'

'Who does?' I said.

'My second cousin, you brute,' she screamed. 'Where else should she live with those sinuses of hers?'

After a moment's silent contemplation on matters geographical and medical I was bound to admit to myself that in this particular case Droitwich Spa was infinitely preferable to Doncaster.

Beryl went to the drinks tray, poured herself a tumbler of neat horseradish sherry, swigged it back in a single gulp and continued:

'I've always been an avid sports fan – a watcher rather than a doer.

'Not that I ever minded playing sport as a girl.

'What stuck in my gullet was the showers.

'All those verrucas and incipient nipples.'

She poured herself another tumbler of sherry and a faint red flush slowly began to suffuse itself over her cheeks.

'And so I watched sport rather than participated,' she said.

'My first love was grass court tennis. Oh, those lovely players on the telly with their masculine thighs and their nine-o'clock shadows. How the names trip off the tongue – Budge Patty, Vic Seixas, Tony Trabert, Virginia Wade.

'I was the world's Number One tennis fan until I discovered that the men in the men's singles smelled under the armpits.

'I was at this tournament in the most sought-after part of Birmingham and I asked this very well-known player for his autograph.

'Well, as he raised his arm to take my navy blue Waterman's fountain pen I suddenly caught this niff and I said:

' "Poo. Put it down. Not today, thank you dear."

'That's why I turned my attention to ice hockey.

'Well, in that environment there's no threat of unsavoury germs or unsightly fungal infections, is there?'

On and on she droned.

My eyelids began to twitch.

My neck sagged.

My earlobes drooped.

My whole body seemed to have been invaded by alien forces over which I had no control.

Were those nightjars nesting in my brain?

Was that a giant sloth crawling slowly up my spine?

On and on and on.

Ice hockey to badminton.

Badminton to lacrosse.

Lacrosse to Cumberland wrestling.

My whole being screamed out with silent agony.

My God, what if she should turn to Trevor Bailey?

It was time for desperate measures.

I stood up.

Before she could interrupt me I said:

'Would you like me to show you my Thing?'

'What?' she gasped. 'What?'

'I shall show you my Thing,' I said.

And I did.

I showed her my Thing.

She collapsed to the floor in a dead faint.

Next morning the Lady Wife accosted me by the pond at the bottom of the garden, where I was entertaining the goldfish with my impersonation of L. Marsland Gander.

'How did you get on with Beryl yesterday?' she said.

'Nicely,' I said.

'I suppose you showed her your Thing?'

I nodded.

She looked over her shoulder slowly and then she said softly:

'Would you like to show it to me?'

I nodded.

'Go on then,' she said.

And so I took out my Thing and showed it to her.

She caressed it gently in her hands.

She rubbed it against her neck.

She held it up to the light and then placed it against her ear.

And she looked up at me out of the tops of her eyes and whispered:

'You've forgotten to wind it up.'

'Blast!' I said.

And I thought to myself: that's the only trouble with a fob watch shaped like the head of Richie Benaud – you never know which ear to put the key into.

CHAPTER TWELVE

The Bird Tapes

There are times during the long and weary plod through The Vale of Tears or the dejected pavilion-bound slink through The Vale of Ambrosial Despair when we receive intelligence that alters forever the whole course of our life.

How well I remember the frisson of naughty excitement when at the age of fifty-three I learnt that nearly all Northamptonshire county cricketers had ginger pubic hair.

The horror is still potent to this very day of the morning I entered innocently the village shop to discover that the proprietor had unilaterally discontinued his popular line in frozen postage stamps.

Imagine the release of guilt and peccancy granted to me, when at the tender age of three and a half my beloved mother of blessed butter-bound memory explained to me so patiently the fundamental difference between the concepts of celibacy and celery – my God, how precious those words would be today to the hierarchy of the Church of Rome.

Imagine my feelings of joy and ecstasy, when I witnessed on the moving television screen the dismantling of the Berlin Wall and the consequent beastlinesses of the Cold War and like millions and millions of my fellow countrymen

I gasped with relief and deliverance and like them I thought to myself:

'Thank God, never again will we have inflicted on us another book by the odious John le Carré.'

Milestones in our lives.

The mark of the tramp on the prim and respectable suburban gatepost.

The leg cock of the lolling dog against stern-spined lamp-post.

But none of these is to compare in impact or significance with the historic material I have in my possession.

Let me calm myself for a moment, dear readers, before revealing them to you.

Let me compose myself by casting my gaze over the old familiar and comforting rustic vistas of Witney Scrotum.

Look.

There in her front garden old Grannie Swanton is breaking up yet another ex-Indian Navy corvette.

Look.

See the Tufnell twins.

How radiant and serenely happy they seem as they depth-charge the bus shelter and stretch piano wire head-high outside the main entrance of the Jug and Arlott.

And look.

Gooch, the village blacksmith, is sitting placidly in the horse trough eating his mid-morning elevenses of curried bellows and poached branding irons.

Enough. Enough.

Refreshed and refurbished it is time for me to devote myself to 'my material'.

First and foremost I have to state that I am not in a position 'to reveal my sources'.

Suffice it to say that to the best of my knowledge they are impeccable and totally reliable.

Never mind the Zinoviev Letter.

Disregard the Trevor-Roper diaries as personally authenticated by Adolf Hitler.

Pay no attention to the leaked billet doux sent by Mr Keith Fletcher to Mrs Ivy Tyldesley of 'Coronation Street'.

These are but small beer compared with . . .

Wait for it, my friends.

. . . compared with the Dickie Bird Tapes.

Here before we get into the 'nitty-gritty' of this priceless, provocative and, yes, sensational material is a brief sweetener, a piquant hors d'oeuvres to whet the appetite.

H.D. 'Dickie' Bird is speaking to an unknown and unheard caller on the talking telephone.

People of a sensitive disposition are advised to remain firmly seated in a darkened lifeboat with a bottle of eau de Aggers smelling salts and a luminous copy of the celebrated *Playboy* eight-page centre spread of the nude Mr Merv Kitchen.

So here goes.

Close your eyes, cover your knees with Marmite, rest your feet in a bowl of Ambrosia creamed rice and imagine you are listening to the dulcet, lilting tones of Mr H.D. 'Dickie' Bird.

'Hullo . . . Hullo . . . Who's that . . . Pardon? Would you repeat that and say it again? . . . It's me. Dickie. Pardon? . . .

'Hullo . . . Hullo . . . who's that? Is it the dry cleaner's? . . . Pardon? . . . It's me. Dickie . . . Oh . . . Oh . . . No, I'm right out of Hoover bags at the moment. I think you must have the wrong number.'

Sensational, eh?

Talk about drama in high places?

The scum of the tabloid press would have every right to call it 'dynamite'.

And from whence did it come?

I can't tell. I mustn't.

I promised. I gave my word.

I am an officer and gentleman.

I have served King and country faithfully and loyally.

I have been entrusted with secrets of the most sensitive and delicate nature.

My honesty and integrity are unquestioned.

I would not dream of . . .

Miss Roebuck gave them to me.

As you know, she has certain journalistic pretensions of a somewhat meagre nature and to this end contributes slightly risqué bi-monthly articles to the trade journal of the Water Cress Growers' Association of Great Britain.

It was in this capacity that the tapes came into her possession.

I did not question her further, for when she presented them to me furtively during the luncheon interval of Mrs Gatting's annual barn dance and arsonists' get-together, there was an excited flush to the front of her cinnamon angora twinset and noticeable throbbing to her cultured pearls, which suggested an imminent attack of the swooning much prevalent among suckling sows in agricultural establishments in the environs of Witney Scrotum.

'Play them,' she gasped. 'You must play them at once.'

I returned home immediately, snubbing, I regret to say, Miss Gower in the ladies-excuse-me musical hokey cokey.

I repaired to my study and examined closely the objects pressed into my hand by Miss Roebuck.

Unfortunately the bloody things did not fit into my trusty wind-up radiogram and I was about to consign them as part of the Lady Wife's loathsome. Bedlington terriers' afternoon snack, when the Commodore entered and apprised me of their identity.

'They're thingermejigs,' he said.

'Ah,' I said, immensely impressed by his obvious profound and detailed knowledge of the world of modern technology.

'I've got a whatsitsname you can play them on. Come with me to the summer house and we'll see what's what.'

I complied with his suggestion and together we made our way to that delectable building at the bottom of his garden with its redolent smell of stale marsupials and world-weary light baritones.

He produced a contraption from under a pile of slowly maturing underpants he had first 'laid down' in the autumn of 1977 and said:

'It's a doodah. Dear old Bruce Woodcock of *The Times* brought it back for me after the last meeting of the Edmundo Ros Fan Club.'

But what does it do?' I said.

'It plays things,' said the Commodore.

'What sort of things?' I said.

'Clickings and screechings and wheezings and strange stentorian barks.'

'Ah,' I said. 'The courtship song of Mr Mervyn Hughes.'

The Commodore nodded and said gravely:

'I'll show you how it works.'

Seven hours later we managed to fit into the machine the miniature, transparent toilet rolls which Miss Roebuck had thrust into my grasp earlier in the day.

The Commodore, rather nervously I thought for one of a nautical bent and maritime pretensions, pressed a button and to our amazement, to our absolute astonishment, there emanated from the machine the following conversation:

DICKIE BIRD: 'Hullo. Hullo. Who's that? Is it the wool shop? . . . Pardon? Yes that's right. It's me. Dickie . . .

'Pardon? . . . I'm not doing too badly, thank you. Well, that's apart from my sciatica and the sicky headaches I always get when I'm standing at Worksop. I've got a slight attack of biliousness, too. Well, it were asking for trouble eating those liquorice bootlaces at . . . Pardon? . . . Pardon?

'No. That's cleared up now. I've started using this ointment recommended by Sir Andrew Lloyd-Webster and it's done wonders. I'm using my homeopathic hot water bottle too, and it's . . . Pardon? What's that you say?'

At this there was a sound of sighing and sobbing and heavy breathing and then came a voice, soft, yielding, well-bred and crackling with deep emotion.

WELL-BRED VOICE: 'It's all been a sham, Dickie. It's all been an act. These past years – they've been horrific.

'All these humiliations. All these degradations. I've not courted publicity. I've not been unfaithful. How dare they say I've been unfaithful?

'I've tried my hardest to make a go of things. God knows, I've tried. But they've always been against me, the establishment.

'All those haughty stuffed-shirts with their plummy accents and their MCC ties and their dowdy wives looking down their noses at me. I can never do right in their eyes.

'And there's the press hounding my every move, dogging my every footstep. And the photographers prying into the deepest recesses of my private life.

'It's been intolerable, Dickie. It's been a nightmare. I'm so miserable. I'm so wretched.'

The tape ended.

We looked at each other silently, the Commodore and I.

The voice was unmistakable.

We had heard it thousands of times on the talking wireless.

The person in question, slim, elegant, bashful and winsome and always immaculately turned out had rarely been off the screens of our moving television.

Yes, dear readers, it was none other than Mr E.R. 'Elizabeth Regina' Dexter.

As always on these occasions I thought to myself – thank God Mr Ken Higgs resisted so firmly the temptations to marry into the Royal Family.

Our hearts turned over for that lovely creature.

Why had the establishment dragged him from a life of simple, decent obscurity and thrust him into the spotlight glare of strident publicity?

How tragic to witness the souring of his fresh virginal charms.

How beastly to see him turned 'before our very eyes' into a sulky pouting recluse.

And then I suddenly remembered.

Saintly men!

My God, this very day we were to be visited by Dr F.S. Trueman, Emeritus Professor of Difficult Sums and Dropped Aitches at the University of Bramall Lane.

Let me explain.

For some reason totally unfathomable to me the Lady Wife has taken 'quite a shine' to the brute and for the past seven years has invited him to spend a weekend with us here at Witney Scrotum.

The agony of it.

The misery.

I'd have sooner spent seven years suspended upside down from the rear end of a barrage balloon over a sewerage works in the centre of Congleton.

But he was due to arrive and I had to be 'on hand' to greet him.

Reluctantly I left the Commodore's summer house and returned sloth-like to my house.

As usual Dr Trueman arrived in his chauffeur-driven motorcycle combination and announced:

'I were just talking to young Sir Jack 'Obbs before I set off.'

The Lady Wife drooled shamelessly at him and rattled her kneecaps.

'Were you indeed?' she said.

'Oh aye,' said the good doctor. 'And Wilfred Rhodes. And George 'Irst. And Sir Leonard 'Utton. I always call him Leonard. I only grovel when I'm in the presence of peers of the realm and lady show jumpers. Has someone farted?'

We quartered him for the night in the dog kennel.

'That's champion for me,' he said. 'I can't stand these 'ere swanky Southern beds with fitted sheets and moth balls under the bolsters. They didn't 'ave them in my day.

'Just give me a bale of straw and a bag of Bonios and I'll be as right as rain.'

Next morning over breakfast our distinguished guest surveyed the provender and said:

'We didn't 'ave breakfasts like this in the old days. These youngsters – they wouldn't know a decent pork sausage if it stood up and bit them in the arse.'

I expected the Lady Wife to 'explode'.

But she didn't.

She just looked at him with a look of nauseating adoration in her piggy little eyes as she cut his fried bread into soldiers and taught him with infinite patience how to use his fork.

'Nay,' said Doctor Trueman. 'Breakfast isn't like it was in my day becorrse and owing to the fact that these youngsters don't practise. They think they know it all, do these youngsters.

'Look at Andrew Caddick and 'is big ears. In my days you wasn't allowed to 'ave big ears in Yorkshire if you was a fast bowler. You 'ad them amputated at birth by Herbert Sutcliffe and Percy 'Olmes. In my day . . .'

I fled to the Commodore's summer house.

He greeted me with a conspiratorial wink and said:

'I've found some more. On the tape. Right at the end. Listen.'

He pressed the button and of an instant I heard those familiar tones droning on endlessly like a recently castrated chain saw.

FAMILIAR GHASTLY VOICE: 'Nah then your Royal 'Ighness, if I might be allowed to venture such familiar tones with your good self, I were just talking to your Prince Hedward and he were telling me you was in a spot of bother regarding 'Er Majesty and old buggerlugs with the bald patch and the polo player's piles.

'Well, take my advice, luv, and make it up with 'ubbie. Take a tip from me and George Statham. We 'ad our little tiffs. Course we bloody did. Nag, nag, nag with 'im, it were. Morning, noon and night. I couldn't do nothing right. I were only talking to W.G. Grace this morning and 'e told me . . .'

At this the Lady Wife burst into the summer house.

'I can't stand it,' she cried. 'Enough is enough. He's eaten all the spider plants and garrotted the goldfish. I've booted him out.'

I was delighted.

I was thrilled beyond measure.

But there was only one cloud on the horizon.

Next year I fear she will invite Miss Joanna Lumley.

And her bloody teeth.

I was only talking to Neville Cardus this morning and he told me . . .

CHAPTER THIRTEEN

When Winter Comes

And so the season dribbles painlessly and somnolently to its close.

No merlin swoop on broad and rolling Rumsey Downs.

No flacker and flick of wagtail on suppling River Buse.

Swift screech long gone from soaring skies above Botham's Gut.

Winter comes. Winter comes.

The cricket pitch, worn, weary and near terminally pock-marked with the ceaseless indentations made by the key to Sir Geoffrey Boycott's outside lavatory, returns to the long slumbers of 'the ruler of th'inverted year' to be disturbed only by the nocturnal ablutions activities of the village idiot and flasher, old Ben Stansgate, and by the ghastly banshee howls of defrocked Minor Counties umpires, swinging in the breeze on ghostly MCC gibbets.

It is time to top up old Grannie Swanton with anti-freeze.

The toad circumcisers' bradawls are mulling in Oslear's coke-fired complaints box.

The Tufnell twins are already practising ski jumping from the roof of the golf ball museum.

It is sad and doleful, I suppose, to see the end of summer and the delights of sitting nude in the bath listening to

'Gardeners' Question Time' on the talking wireless, but this autumn in particular gives us special reasons for rejoicing.

I refer, of course, to the ordination of our new, young and handsome curate, the Reverend Michael Atherton.

His presence in Witney Scrotum has already caused many a flutter among the hearts of chaste young maidens in the senior citizens aromatherapy unit, and rumour has it that Mistress Frindall from the temperance launderette has already knitted him one of her special scorers' straitjackets in a most fetching shade of Aggers aquamarine primrose.

It is my firm opinion that we have made 'quite a catch' in young Atherton.

I like the cut of his jib.

I like the way he crooks his little finger when he is picking Mr Alec Stewart's nose at vespers.

I like the way he forgets to take the coat hanger out of his shirt when he is fielding second slip at matins.

I like his shy, pink, gummy smile as he calls for minor adjustments to the chancel screen at the reredos end.

I like the slow lumber of his sermons as he exhorts us to 'get our heads down' and 'keep good line and length' and never let the nig nogs get us down.

I haven't the faintest idea what he's talking about but at least he doesn't fidget in the pulpit and gives the congregation a decent drinks interval every five minutes.

I feel certain he is unlikely to hold 'much truck' with Don 'Sir Oswald' Mosey and his Junior Blackshirts, who have recently caused so much trouble in the Jug and Arlott in relation to the newly installed Gunn and Moore condom machines.

It is no surprise, therefore, to learn from my current edition of *Who's Who?* (the Northern version, *'Oo's 'Oo?*)

that he comes from a 'good background', humble but honest, poor but thrifty.

He was born in the pleasant, leafy, prosperous suburb of Moss Side in the City of Manchester, but then after the dramatic and sudden collapse of the pumice stone market the family, their fortune vanished overnight, were forced to move to one of the foulest, cess-pitted, hovel-ridden slums in the whole of the United Kingdom – Prestbury in the county of Cheshire.

His parents were determined that this would not drag him down.

He would not follow in the footsteps of the teenage louts and vandals they saw hanging around gas-lit, snot-sodden street corners at nights and find himself in later life reduced to a precarious career of examining table legs on 'Antiques Road Show' or working as deputy keeper of Persian watermarks at the British Museum.

They would forsake the annual three-week holiday at Zermatt.

They would sell the precious bound volumes of Playfair Cricket annuals.

Thus did they scrimp.

Thus did they scrape.

But the task seemed hopeless.

Misfortune dogged their every footstep.

His father, moonlighting in the brass section of the Hallé Orchestra, was mugged of his trombone halfway through the second over of Beethoven's Third.

His mother fell off a double-decker bus in St Peter's Square and shattered beyond redemption three Etruscan vases she had bought in a 'discontinued line' sale at British Home Stores.

Despair. Misery.

And then Lady Luck stepped in.

Triumph. Jubilation.

Young Michael won third prize in the *Sun* bingo competition – an open scholarship to Manchester Grammar School.

But their joy was short-lived.

Although young Michael was outstanding at his studies he was constantly mocked and derided by his fellow pupils as he sat hunched up in mental arithmetic classes dressed in Ken Higgs hand-me-downs and scratching his sums on a hot plate taken from the top of Cyril Washbrook's third change Aga cooker.

No wonder he left school at the age of thirteen, a sad, forlorn, stoop-shouldered figure suspicious of badgers, nervous of vacuum cleaners and terrified of girls with 'things' on the front of their chests.

Like so many young men who in their formative years have been derided, despised, reviled and humiliated and thus lost self-respect, self-confidence, the will to live, their faith in the essential goodness of their fellow men to the point of hating them, despising them, wishing that every man jack of them was wiped from the face of the earth to fester in the steaming pits of eternal perdition, there were only two options open to him – to become captain of Derbyshire County Cricket Club or accept ordination into the Church of England.

He chose the latter.

We will gloss over his student days at theological college in Southport where in off-duty hours he struck up a firm and lasting friendship with Red Rum.

Suffice it to say that he made a 'more than favourable' impression on the Venerable William Alley and endeared himself to all with his missionary work among distressed starters' assistants at Haydock Park.

He completed his studies successfully, despite somewhat disappointing marks in comparative religion and cake icing, and was ordained at Liverpool Cathedral by the Right Reverend David Shepherd, who charmed all present by hopping from leg to leg during the singing of Hymn 111.

His first appointment was in the West Indies.

There he took up a position as personal chaplain to a band of impoverished, subjugated white settlers wandering hand to mouth from island to island, reviled, despised, taunted, mocked and subjected to torrents of vitriolic abuse and shameless unprovoked attack from every quarter.

The young Atherton acted swiftly.

Almost before he had time to unpack his Donald Duck pyjamas and his electric train set he had organised outdoor community hymn singing, late night bible readings and mass baptisms and in 'next to no time' his charges were restored to a state of simple natural dignity and were able to sleep soundly at nights untroubled by dreams of snarling, snow white teeth, curried slip cradles and the ghastly unctuous dronings of Sir Geoffrey Boycott.

And thus 'mission completed' he has taken up residence here with us in Witney Scrotum.

We welcome him with open arms.

Our joy is tempered, though, for sadly we have seen the last of our much-revered and much-loved village blacksmith, Gooch.

After a lifetime's devoted service to the inhabitants of Witney Scrotum, rounding up stray Belisha beacons and eating up our surplus supplies of horse troughs, he has gone to 'pastures new'.

Rumour has it that he has taken up a position as chief voice coach to the Royal National Theatre, where I am certain he will achieve instant distinction as being the only permanent member of staff able to read Dame Maggie Smith's flipper.

That sadness apart, there is much pleasure to be derived from dressing myself in mauve plus fours and inflatable spats, settling down in the drawing room with its unique collection of E.R. 'Elizabeth Regina' Dexter-autographed death masks and ruminating with pleasure on the delights of the past summer.

It has indeed been a rich and fruitful season of achievement and success for some of the more illustrious luminaries here in our beloved village.

In June and July old Squire Brearley set out on his annual expedition of discovery equipped as usual with nothing more than a camel, half a loaf of Hovis, a musical compass, a two-way commode and the collected works of Mr Christopher Martin-Jenkins (edible edition).

This year, Thesiger-like, he ventured with the utmost courage and heroism into one of this island's most remote, savage and unrelentingly hostile regions.

I refer, of course, to The Empty Quarter – also known to the more intrepid and esoteric of explorers as Glamorgan.

The old Squire returned home, blistered with heat, ravaged by thirst and hunger and festooned from head to foot in the dregs of Brain's best dark beer.

Yet he was in high spirits and confessed he had never felt better since the day he was awarded an honorary degree in Viticulture and Sight Screen Maintenance at the University of Trent Bridge in the summer of 1876.

'I have,' he announced with considerable dramatic impact to the villagers assembled in the Merv Kitchen annexe of the hoof repository warehouse, 'discovered a tribe of previously unknown cricketers.'

We gasped with astonishment.

Deaconess Victoria Marks let out one of her gulping, nervous cackles and fell into a dead swoon and was only revived when she was kicked soundly in the ribs by PC 'Percy' Pocock and given the kiss of life by the Commodore's personal stirrup pump.

At length the silence was broken by Ma Botham from the Home for Retired Pantomime Dames and Redundant Car Boot Salesmen.

'I know what they be, them cricketers,' she said.

'Old Squire Brearley have discovered a tribe what is unique in the whole of the world – not a single one of them is eligible to play cricket for England.'

We gasped with astonishment again.

If this were true, had a dastardly precedent been set for the coming season?

Would Señor Placido Domingo not, after all, open England's bowling with Devon Malcolm?

Would Herr Barbra Streisand be denied her long-cherished ambition of taking over the gloves from Jack Russell?

You could have heard a Zimmer frame drop as old Squire Brearley rose to resume his speech.

Even old Grampy Barrie Meyer was aroused from his reveries of how he had given out three Australian batsmen caught behind when they were innocently eating chocolate-covered giraffe's toenails in the visitors' dressing room at the Oval.

And then the Squire spoke thus in his familiar rococo style with the ancient thatch of his beard encrusted with Daddy sauce and Fabergé peanut shells.

'They were dear, primitive people, this tribe of simple cricketers,' he said.

'Their absolute trust in one was profoundly moving and brought unashamed tears to my tired old eyes, long-accustomed to sights of unrestrained depravity and rapaciousness in the dressing room at Headingley.

'We presented them with trinkets – reconstituted jock straps, half-chewed bails, well-sucked thigh pads and clock-work cricket bags – and the glee with which they ate them made my shins throb with ecstasy and my truss croon with near carnal lust.

'After they had daubed us with woad and affixed votive offerings to our private parts, we watched them play a cricket match and I was instantly bewitched by the naivety of purpose and the unsullied *joie de vivre* they displayed in conducting themselves in a manner totally dedicated to bringing pleasure to the spectators.

'With my own eyes I actually saw batsmen who struck the ball cleanly and fluently.

'I saw bowlers who attacked the wicket and seemed to be sponsored by a fervent desire to dismiss their opponents.

'Unbelievably I saw fielders who displayed boundless treasures of enthusiasm and athleticism, of swiftness and dexterity and passion and commitment.'

At this the lugubrious Fletcher stood up, emptied the ferret droppings from his carpet slippers, eased a ruck in his shroud and said:

'Yeah, but they're a load of Taffs, ain't they?

'I seen enough of that lot of sheep-shaggers when I was learning Sir Harry Secombe how to eat his soup proper at the Cricket Writers' Dinner and Annual Piss-Up at the Nawab of Pataudi's takeaway dahn the Edgware Road.

'We don't want a load of bleeding foreigners cluttering up our national side, do we?

'Old Hicky and Smithy and Lamby and Devon and Chris and Hussein and Lofty Caddick'd do their bloody nuts, wouldn't they?

'It's bad enough having a captain what comes from the Norff and don't need no help in eating his All Bran with the proper fork.'

I think of that evening now as I stand by the window of my study looking out into the soft, owl-fested night with the silver sliver of the moon scudding at the lean-limbed clouds and the . . .

Hold on.

I see a figure flitting through the shadows.

It is a male figure.

And he is holding the hand of a companion.

It is a female companion.

Good God, it can't be.

It is.

Yes, it most certainly is.

It is the Reverend Atherton and he is holding the hand of Miss Roebuck from the dog biscuit shop.

Oh joy.

Oh ecstasy.

My fondest wish has been granted.

The two dear creatures are going 'to make a go of things'.

Do I hear the joyous chime of wedding bells?

Do I hear the pitter-pat of tiny feet?

Atherton and Roebuck – what a union!

Let the angels sing.

Let the heavenly hosts rejoice.

Let mariners far out at sea send up maroons and flares.

Let redundant coal miners rattle the keys of their automatic Volvos.

Let the lost tribes beyond Offa's Dyke build bonfires and sacrifice Ossie Wheatley on a mattress of burning bulrushes and the begging letters of Mr Tony Lewis.

Atherton and Roebuck.

Roebuck and Atherton.

Every conjunction is soothing to the soul and pleasing to the spirit.

There is just one thing, though.

When they have issue, we must pray fervently that it is delivered by the natural childbirth method.

We don't want Raymond Illingworth sticking his bloody oar in, do we?

CHAPTER FOURTEEN

Farewell,
My Lovelies

The day of the death of my late and much-loathed father is forever engraved on my memory.

It was either a Monday or a Thursday.

My pet rabbit, Hornby, died at 3.17 am on the morning of the second Tuesday after Belgian Independence Day.

The garden was full of midges.

Inchcape-Muncer was killed on Christmas Day.

When we returned from hols the headmaster announced at chapel:

'It is with deep and profound regret that I have to announce the death of . . . of . . . of . . .'

He had to refer to his notes.

Poor Inchcape-Muncer.

His greatest ambition in life was to bat number seven for The Free Foresters.

When I was a small boy, I was constantly reminded of the prospect of death.

'Just think of all the people in the past who've died,' my father used to say to me.

I would lower my head, shuffle my feet and scratch my elbows, and he would scream:

'Think, boy. Think, God damn you.'

I did.

It made a lot of sense.

The following obituaries of a cricketing nature make even more sense to me now as I sit in my garden at Witney Scrotum and watch the Commodore's wall-eyed cat slinking after the blackbirds in the laurel's sticky hems and listening to the mew of the hunting buzzard and sensing the scream of the crouching vole.

I hope they make sense to you, dear readers.

BISPHAM Dame Valerie
Received her DBE in 1947 for services to the tea interval.
Invented the quick-release potted meat sandwich and the disposable fairy cake.
Pioneer of the reversible quiche.
Dame Valerie is survived by her colander.

PONTIAK Frederick Otago
Cricket explorer and anthropologist.
First man to make a single-handed crossing of the Oval in winter.
Discovered the first known example of homo cricketus in ancient charnel pits at Pudsey.
Through the application of carbon dating techniques and DNA genetic analysis it was later identified as Mr Raymond Illingworth.

HEGARTY, Walter Vivian Tirpitz
Celebrated cricket transvestite.
Dressed as Queen Mary whilst inspecting the Australian tourists at Lord's in 1948 made the immortal remark to Mr Keith Miller:

'Now then, bacon balls, who do you reckon's going to win the 3.30 at Kempton Park?'

BAKTERIA, The Goolam of
Afghanistan umpire and owner of the world's finest and most extensive private collection of cricket erotica. Among his most priceless possessions are three Gunn and Moore cricket bats in the style of early Retford phallic, the original Aubrey Beardsley illustrations for the 1922 Wisden Cricketers' Almanack (Lysistra edition) and the complete collection of dried testicles as shed each year by New Zealand cricket commentators. Died in his sleep whilst inspecting his latest acquisition, a lithograph of the Lascaux cave painting entitled: 'Frederick Trueman at Toilet with Two Mammoths, a Sabre-toothed Tiger and Mr Mervyn Kitchen.'
He is succeeded to his title by Mr Jonathan Agnew.

HUMPER, Henry
Distinguished baggage master.
Famous for losing the entire luggage of the MCC touring party to Australia, 1928–29.
According to research scholars of 'the summer game' this explains why Mr George Duckworth kept wicket against a South Australian Country XI wearing nothing but ladies' bicycle clips and Mr Douglas Jardine's snuffbox.
On his retirement he became a freelance left luggage office attendant.
He is survived by a gents' attaché case with the initials Rev. R.J. St P. W. with tooth marks on the handle.

KITTERTON, Nancy Maude
Much-loved landlady and confidante of generations of

county cricketers.

O.L. writes:

'I first met Ma Kitterton when I was staying at her lodgings as a young middle order batsman and occasional seamer in the summer of 1923.

'I was struck at once by her infectious gaiety.

'She called all her lodgers "dearie" or "my boys" and was attentive to our every need.

'For example, in her basement she had what she called her gym, where she encouraged us to "work out" and get the stiffness out of her limbs after a long day in the field at the Oval or Lord's.

'I myself personally never availed myself of the facilities, but our senior professional at the time averred that they did him "a power of good".

'However, I did notice that he was inclined to wince more than somewhat when struck on the sit-upon by the second new ball and rarely took off his underpants in public.

'I was particularly impressed by the friendliness of her numerous nieces, to whom we were introduced immediately on arrival at her establishment.

'Owing to the shortage of accommodation we were often asked if we would be so kind as to share our sleeping quarters with these charming young ladies.

'Having been in the Boy Scouts for most of my formative years I was only too happy to "do my best" and oblige.

'I particularly remember a distant cousin of Ma Kitterton's on the Goanese side of the family, who arrived unexpectedly late at night at the lodgings in some distress having mislaid her sleeping apparel in a taxi cab "somewhere in Port Said", where she had been engaged in good works of a missionary nature.

'I volunteered to lend her my spare pair of pyjamas but she insisted on sleeping *au naturel* owing to the fact that she was allergic to green and maroon stripes.

'We spent a most entertaining night together during which she gave me a most novel demonstration of the technique of keeping my end up in a tight situation.

'I confess I had never come across that particular method previously despite extensive perusal of my extensive collection of MCC coaching manuals.

'Next morning I was only too happy to give the young lady £7 2s 3d for a cup of tea.'

Ma Kitterton died during a *bal masqué* at the Wombwell Cricket Lovers' Society.

JAKEMAN, Ernest Vidal
Official barber in residence, Lord's, 1921–1977.
First man to give a DA haircut to Sir Pelham Warner.
Personal back-comber to Sir 'Gubby' Allen.
Creator of the 'Dreadlock' look for Lt Colonel J.R. Stephenson.

BUTTERWORTH, Percy Hubert Laxman
The slowest eater in first class cricket.
Once took five hours thirty-seven minutes to eat a ham salad at Hove, Sussex versus Cambridge University. As a result MCC devised the current rules regulating the duration of tea and luncheon adjournments, the so-called 'Butterworth Amendment'.

The only exception to this is the consumption of game pie and plovers' eggs during the Cheltenham Festival and the application of covers to protect fellow diners whilst Mr Raymond Illingworth is eating polony and cream crackers. On his retirement from the first class game

Butterworth became chief laxative taster to Mr Frederick Trueman.

He died from an overdose of gregory powder.

QUESTED, Daphne Iris

Longest-serving agony aunt on Wisden Cricketers' Almanack. Third daughter of N.F. Wafting Esq. of Andover and second daughter of Mrs Roderick Barusch of Hammerfest, Daphne Quested was educated privately in Bolton and The Hague. After a brief and unhappy marriage to Mungo Quested (golfer and gentleman seismologist) she joined the Wisden organisation in 1922 with special responsibility for the Index, 'Ponsford, W.H. (Aust) to Public schools, highest score.'

Within seven years she had progressed to the post of chief compiler, Plunkett Shield Winners.

Her 'big break' occurred in 1937 on the retirement 'under distressing circumstances' of W.G. Mumford-Saggers, the celebrated Auntie Gladys.

It was a 'difficult act' to follow but Daphne Quested with typical bonhomie and enthusiasm took on her new responsibilities with verve and gusto and soon her canary yellow Rudge autocycle was a familiar sight in the staff bicycle shed.

Within 'next to no time' she had established herself as 'a firm favourite' with her multitude of admiring readers in her role as Auntie Judith, where her advice ranged from the treatment of stumper's acne to agoraphobia among Minor Counties umpires.

To give an example of her finest work with its unique insights and sympathetic understanding we reproduce the following:

'Dear Auntie Judith,

'Please, please, can you help?

'I am in total despair and desolation.

'For the past forty or so years I have been desperately and madly in love with one of the finest men it has ever been my privilege to meet.

'Let me tell you something about this gorgeous and wonderful creature.

'He has captained his county. He has captained his country. He is one of the finest writers on cricket ever to have put pen to paper and is currently without any doubt the world's outstanding television cricket commentator.

'And yet I have suddenly fallen out of love with him.

'What oh what am I to do?'

Auntie Judith's reply went thus:

'Dear Tony,

'Do nothing.

'It is quite common for men of your age to fall out of love with themselves.'

MUSTARD, Lionel
Leader of the nude cricket movement.
Vegetarian off spinner and inventor of the organic matting wicket.
Died of exposure, Old Trafford.

FLICH, Wystan Bernard
Cricket couturier.
Designer of David Gower's wedding gown.

CHAPTER FIFTEEN

The Perfect Day

I am often asked by that emaciated vileness, Tinniswood, my idea of the perfect day.

Well, the answer to that is simplicity itself.

It goes thus:

Mind your own business, you verminous, malodorous, Northern scum with your concave shins, your uncouth teeth, your bloodshot eyes and the slow drear of your weedy, piping, catarrh-sodden voice.

How the brute cringes.

How he cowers and blubbers into the dank darkness of his snot-straggled beard.

Nonetheless there are moments of quiet contemplation, when my thoughts stray like primrose petals in a weak spring gale and I indulge in fantasies pertaining to the notion of the perfect day.

With some misgivings, I am bound to confess, I am prepared to share them with you, dear readers.

Against my better judgement I am willing to pander to your insatiable curiosity and your voracious nosiness in order to bring a ray of comfort, a glint of hope and solace into the drab of your wretched, soul-sobbing existence as you struggle to come to terms with the basic, all-pervading, throat-thrumming problems of your everyday lives – how to fix new adhesive binding to the handles of your potato peelers and how to address a deputy circuit judge whom you have come across accidentally in a mixed sauna in Launceston.

So here goes.

Chums – that would be the order of the day.

Twenty-four hours of peace, tranquillity and pensive concordance spent in the company of dear and precious friends who have enriched the warmest cockles of my life with the toe-tingling warmth of their propinquity.

But whom to invite?

More pertinently – whom not to invite?

Well, for a start Prince Charles is out.

I don't care how desperate he is for human company.

I will not budge from my inflexible rule of never entertaining in my home a person who is liable to fall off the piano stool and jam his ears in the scullery meat safe.

And as for Lucinda Lambton – there's another stinker I'd veto without hesitation.

Did you see her on the moving television, prowling like a dyspeptic otter hound through the Paris home of Mrs Simpson and our beloved Duke of Wisden?

Well, she's not doing it in my house.

I will not tolerate her rooting through my sock drawer, sniffing my underpants and doing rude things in the wardrobe with my waterproof plus fours.

And just think of the loathsome Bottomleys, Peter and her husband, Virginia!

Can you imagine anything more ghastly than witnessing La Serenissima sitting on her partner's Adam's apple and canoodling with his BUPA car sticker?

Who else would be off my guest list?

Simple.

Greengrocers with bad table manners, manufacturers of flock wallpaper, bald lacrosse players, ex-King Constantine of Greece, designers of sardine tins, the entire cast of 'The Archers', L. Marsland Gander and anyone who ever bowled out Winston Place.

This leaves me with but one person in the whole wide world whose company I would cherish and treasure.

No, it is not Jaroslav Drobny.

No, it is not the chief flautist of the Bournemouth Sinfonietta.

It is, of course, my dear old chum, the Commodore.

What a sublimely perfect day we would have together.

The house would be deserted.

The Lady Wife and her detestable Bedlington terriers would be in quarantine in kennels somewhere in the remoter regions of Baluchistan.

The mice would be on their annual holiday in old Squire Brearley's indoor bottle bank.

And from the window of my study we would see Grannie Swanton working happily in her front garden, defusing yet another unexploded German land mine.

We would yarn about the good old days – snuffling, hard-spined trams in a wheezing London peasouper, the rasp and crackle of nesting corncrake on wind-trilled downland wheat fields, the howl of agony as the Lady Wife 'measured her length' on a good-humoured duckboard at the Cheltenham Festival.

We would consume snorters.

We would comment on the ills of contemporary society – the demise of the red squirrel and the bus conductor's ticket punch, the persecution of the golden privet, the virtual extinction of piano tuners' goggles.

We would consume more snorters.

We would write poison pen letters to Peru.

We would consume yet more snorters.

We would ring up the duty officer at the British Broadcasting Corporation and complain about people eating with their mouths open on 'Coronation Street'.

We would . . . we would . . . we would consnort more sumers and . . . and . . .

And we would fall into blessed oblivion after burning a hole in the Lady Wife's pyjama case.

This, as told in their own words, is how some distinguished luminaries of the cricket world would spend their perfect day:

KEITH FLETCHER

My perfect day would commence thus:

First of all I would wake up.

It's amazing how often you can forget to do this, isn't it?

I would look around the room carefully, sniff once or twice, examine my private parts and say out loud to myself:

'Oh, goody, goody, I'm not in Darlington.'

Then I should commence to dress.

First of all I would insert my right foot into my right shoe.

Then I would repeat the operation with my other foot, which, if memory serves me correct, is my left one.

Shortly after this I would discover that I had neglected to put on my trousers and would thus be compelled to remove my shoes.

What a berk!

Then I would go downstairs.

Unless, of course, I was residing in a bungalow, which would make the above operation somewhat redundant.

I would go into the kitchen and make myself a nice, cheery cup of tea in the coffee percolator.

Then I would pick up the phone in order to have another of my stimulating chats with that nice lady with the posh voice at Directory Enquiries.

Isn't it amazing how she knows so many numbers?

After this I would do a spot of grouting.

I like grouting.

I think grouting's terrific.

So's picking radishes.

And going through old knitting patterns isn't bad neither.

After going through some old knitting patterns I would repair to the back garden where I would partake of my favourite meal of all time.

My favourite meal of all time is a beaker of grapefruit crush and a plate of chewing gum sandwiches.

At 11.35 am in the morning I would stand up and say:

'I wonder what I'll do next.'

At 3.36 pm in the afternoon I would stand up again and say:

'Oh, sod it.'

And then I would go back to bed.

What a Herbert.

RAYMOND ILLINGWORTH

First of all I should attend matins with my private and personal chaplain, the Rev. Adrian Wingfield-Whatshisname.

He's a bit of a snotty-nosed gink with a lah-di-dah accent and too many teeth, but at least he's not harping on all the time about God like that little turd, Alan Thingermejig, who used to do gardening programmes on the wireless.

I can't stand God. I wouldn't have him in my team at any price. Just imagine him in the dressing room. He'd be forever wittering on about how he'd helped Moses out of a hole and created Freddie Trueman out of nothing bar a bag of cement and half a packet of chocolate digestives.

I'd probably have breakfast with that celebrated American songstress with the big nose, Barbra Whosits.

She reminds me a bit of Fred Rumsey, although I don't think her knockers are in the same league.

Following breakfast I would pay visits on selectorial duties to Old Trafford, Taunton, Sofia Gardens, Canterbury, Trent Bridge and Hove.

After this it would be time for lunch.

This would consist of Yorkshire pudding, followed by Yorkshire pudding with for afters Yorkshire pudding with traditional Yorkshire clotted cream.

I'd then spend the afternoon in the House of Commons, where I have a part-time job as Speaker.

I quite like this job as it enables me to dress up in a wig and black silk stockings and dish out thunderous great bollockings to The Beast of Bolsover, Lady Olga Maitland.

I would then have a pint or two with my old mate, Brian Sewell, and then it'd be time to attend a reception at the Coachmakers' and Coach Harness Makers' Company at Mansion House in honour of Sir Yehudi Doodah, open an exhibition of Finnish watercolourists at the Marlborough Fine Art Gallery, grant an audience to the Ambassadors of

Chad and some other place I can't pronounce without taking my teeth out and then it would be time for tea.

I'm not a big eater when it comes to food so I'd probably make do with a bucket of sweetbreads.

I wonder which part of Fred Rumsey they come from.

After tea it'd be time to meet the missus when she got back from work at the ironmonger's and tell her the good news that I'd picked her to captain England for the next seven years.

I'd like to finish the day off with a slight attack of chickenpox.

IMRAN KHAN

It's so boring.

It's so tedious.

It's one long yawn.

Life, I mean.

England these days is intolerable.

The whole place reeks of the working classes.

You just can't escape them.

Bloody Christopher Martin-Jenkins sleeping in a cardboard box under Waterloo Bridge.

Tony 'Taff' Lewis looking more and more like a Burmese cheroot smuggler every time I see him.

The loathsome Neil Durden-Smith hiring out Judith Chalmers as a charlady in Brixton.

Such a common shower, don't you think?

Oh, for Botham, Trueman and Allan Lamb.

Now there's the real *crème de la crème* for you.

Have you ever seen Freddie and Beefy dancing the night away at Annabel's in their matching broderie anglaise cummerbunds?

Have you ever heard the dulcet tones of dear old Lamby as he stands naked on a Corinth plinth in the moonlight, reciting Byron and Swinburne to the peasantry at Kettering?

Style, my dears.

Breeding.

Oh dear, oh dear, oh dear.

Will this day never end?

I suppose it will.

And then there'll be another one.

And another.

And another.

I think I might as well get up.

It must be time to start tampering with the poppadoms at the family takeaway.

PHILIP TUFNELL

No doubt about it, mates.

My perfect day would be spent entirely and all the time in the company of the bloke what is my greatest hero of all time.

What a geezer!

Bleeding immaculate.

A towering genius.

Talk about talent!

Anyone what says he ain't got none, I'll bonk the swede.

And you better believe it.

Talk about the milk of human kindness!

It's pouring out of his bleeding lugholes.

Talk about intelligence and being clever as well!

He's got certificates for it.

And they ain't been nicked neither.

Talk about being modest and caring and considerate to old ladies and policemen and Bengali waiters and unemployed nig nogs!

They should give him the Nobel Prize for it.

I'd give it him meself, if they sold it at Tesco's with coupons.

Yes, no bleeding doubt about it – Jim Davidson is the greatest.

H.D. 'DICKIE' BIRD

I have pondered long and deep about this matter.

Mind you, I ponder long and deep about everything these days since the untimely demise of the Belisha beacon.

For example, I am in a constant state of tiz-woz when it comes to deciding how many Weetabix to have for my breakfast.

There is a strong case to be made out for having one.

On the other hand I could always go nap and have two.

Then again I could plump for shredded wheat, although I find it tends to get somewhat soggy if you put too much milk on it.

Of course you could always put less milk on it, but then you'd face the risk of getting the hard bits stuck under your dentures.

That's why I always carry in my inside pocket a toothpick in an old Elastoplast tin along with a six-inch metal ruler and a spare packet of Jaffa cakes.

However, these breakfast problems are but mere trifles when it comes to deciding on my idea of the perfect day.

Obviously it would involve the consumption of breakfast cereal somewhere along the line, but there are, I fear, more important considerations to be taken into consideration.

Would I have to book in advance?

Would I get a discount from Wallace Arnold if I took my own bedding?

Would I have to pay a supplement for use of cruet?

Well, I wrote down all the pros and all the cons both for and against on two different sheets of notepaper given to me as a Christmas present two years previously by the late Adlai Stevenson, and after totting them up on my pocket calculator, which incidentally works on portable batteries, I finally made my choice.

It is this:

My perfect day would be spent in an Old Folks' Home, preferably on the Lincolnshire coast, which I always find to be most conducive to good bowel movements.

I would dedicate the whole twenty-four hours to making myself handy and cheering up the old codgers by saying things like:

'Oh, dear oh dear, love, you don't look at all good to me. You've a nasty colour there. Have you got a funny taste in your mouth? You've not been sucking your fingers after applying your ointment, have you? I'd ring for matron immediate if I was you.'

One thing about Old Folks' Homes is that you do get a good class of pustule there.

I'm very fond of pimples and, though I say it myself, I'm quite a connoisseur of boils and eruptions.

I once lanced a boil on Richard Hadlee's neck on the second day at Colwyn Bay and I must say it was the best boil I'd seen on a New Zealand Test cricketer since I don't know when.

What I'd like most about spending a day in an Old Folks' Home is feeding time.

I'd find someone who obviously needed assistance and I'd say:

'Oh, that looks nasty, doesn't it, love? Are you sure the caretaker's dog's not been sick on your plate?'

I'd take them out for walks in their bath chairs, too.

Of course I'd 'see to them' before they left the premises.

I always do to my cricketers.

Before the start of a day's play I go into their dressing rooms and I say:

'Now then, have we all remembered to do our stuff?

'Anyone for tinkles?

'Anyone for biggies?'

You'd be surprised how many forget.

That's why I always carry in my inside pocket in an old Elastoplast tin three corks, one bulldog clip and three neatly-cut-up pages of the *Barnsley Chronicle*.

Any road, after attending to the old folk, blowing up their rubber rings for them and wiping the gravy off their spectacles, I'd take them to see the floral clock and . . .

Do you know, I'm getting bored with this.

Not that I've anything against boredom.

I think boredom can be quite stimulating at times, particularly when you're discussing the problems of trout farming in Madagascar with David Constant.

No, I think I'll abandon the Lincolnshire coast and spend the day in Altrincham.

I've never been to Altrincham.

But then there's always a first time for everything, isn't there?

That's why I always carry in my inside pocket in an old Elastoplast tin a compass, a miniature satellite dish and a return ticket to Hoyland Common.

CHRIS LEWIS

My perfect day?
I'd have to cry off owing to injury.

CHAPTER SIXTEEN

Cricketers' Quiz

Rainy days.

Gloomy days.

Days rasped by a chill-lipped wind.

Days sullen with surly-bellied clouds.

Brooding gale-whipped puddles. Sodden turf. The flap and yaw of raincoat hem. The brolly's listless droop. The flag stiff-strained at the mast.

Perfect weather for cricket, dear readers.

Time to repair forthwith to the pavilion with a much-loved chum to indulge in snorters and the contented sluck of a favourite briar.

Time to yarn about days gone by and the passing of the tram driver's gauntlet.

Time to contemplate the great and abiding mysteries of life.

What do women 'see' in talcum powder?

Why do lady sub-post office mistresses always have segs on their fingers?

Why do owners of pet shops always sleep on one leg?

But hark, I hear you say.

Is there not one vital activity missing from your list?

One activity which lifts man alone above the stinking heaving slime reeking with scavenging beast and agued serpent?

No, dear readers, no.

I have not neglected my duty.

That jewel is to come last in my list to sparkle like a nabob's rubies, to glint like a dowager's diamonds and glitter like Mr Richie Benaud's dentures.

Of course. Of course.

It is the cricketers' quiz.

How this noble edifice has comforted and succoured countless generations of Englishmen in times of direst danger, in times of deepest despair.

In the trenches of Flanders, in the Fuzzy-Wuzzied deserts of Araby, in the festering jungles of Borneo it has taken its place with self-abuse and nose-picking as the only occupation destined to keep men sane and free from the ravages of fear and guilt.

Consider Captain Scott and 'Doc' Wilson in their bleak tent in the God-forsaken icy fastness of Antarctica.

What were the last words spoken by the leader to his faithful cohort?

They were these:

'Don't be a prick all your life. Dicky Bird never played for Lancashire in a million years.'

And so, dear readers, the Commodore and I have prepared for your delight and delectation your own personal cricketers' quiz.

Sit back.

Relax.

Ease the ruck in your underpants.

Have a sniff of your neighbour's socks.

Allow yourselves the sublime luxury of a long slow silent fart.

And enjoy the quiz.

But remember you are Englishmen and no cheating.

Dagos and Wops with fungal infections of the armpits may disregard the above constraint.

THE QUESTIONS

1. FAMOUS FIRST LINES

The world of our beloved 'summer game' has provided English literature with some of its finest most precious jewels. Here I think of the opening sentence of Mr Keith Fletcher's celebrated memoir 'Letters To A Friend From A Sojourn In The West Indies.'

It reads thus:

'Dear Mick

'I haven't had a decent crap for seventeen days.'

Here is a selection of other celebrated first lines from the genre.

Author, please, and title of book.

(a) 'Living and growing up in a row of terraced houses is not nearly as bad as some sociologists and planning authorities would have us believe.'

(b) 'Some marriages, so they say, are made in Heaven. Ours was conceived, the apposite deity presiding, in The Eros.'

(c) 'He was only a young 'un not yet fourteen but he trudged through the snow that February morning like a man.'

(d) 'In July 1908 I made an inauspicious entry into a smoky world. The town of Elland, which is at least favoured by being on the right side of the Pennines and roughly in the centre of the most concentrated industrial area in the world, was too busy making smoke to pay much attention to my arrival.'

(e) 'The tour opened at St Pancras on the morning of 17 September and a very big crowd gathered to wish the players good luck.'

(f) 'When I was a schoolboy in Cirencester the school was playing a local side skippered by a veteran cricketer of some renown.'

(g) 'The first time my name appeared in a newspaper was about 1921 when this paragraph was published in a New South Wales weekly called *Smith's Weekly*:
' "Saw a curious thing at a junior cricket match at Bowral recently." '

(h) 'When I had come back to England from India on demobilisation, like many another I had gone up to Olympia and been given my suit – quite a good suit it was, too, I remember. Certainly in the spring of 1946 it was a good suit. Then you were lucky to be able to get one at all.'

(i) 'Tennessee Williams remains in America which probably accounts for the fact that no dramatist has yet uttered the terrible frustration of county captains as a vehicle for modern tragedy.'

(j) 'There is going to be no introduction to this book.'

2. MIDDLE NAMES

My father of late and loathsome memory did not bother to give me a middle name. Indeed it was only after lengthy and heated discussions with his wine merchant that he gave me a first name.

Cricketers as a breed bear no such affliction.

To whom do the following middle names belong?

Cleophas
John
Babulas
Arras
Falconer
Charles
Laxman
John
John
Baddeley
Augustine
St Aubrun
Baxter
John
Sewards
Berrange
Laxman
Leopold
de Courcey
Amwin
Ethelbert
Windridge
John

George
John
Subramanya
John
Gilbert
John
Samuel
Berry
Standish

3. BIRTH PLACES

Owing to an unsightly combination of whisky stains, termite predations and congealed emu droppings on my birth certificate I am unable to determine the exact place of my birth.

The Lady Wife will brook no such prevarication.
She maintains that it is Neuschwanstein.
I take the view that it is more likely to be Stockport.
Cricketers have no such problems.

Who was born at the following places?

Ulverston, Cumbria
30 March 1940

Tunbridge Wells
1 April 1957

Witney Scrotum
1 January 1914

Bangor, Caernarvonshire
24 September 1934

Sandyford, Stoke-on-Trent
28 March 1941

Clayton-le-Moors
28 March 1941

Rawtenstall
7 December 1914

Keating New Town
17 November 1994

Worcester
20 May 1946

Nairobi
18 September 1958

Port of Spain
2 October 1873

Deligun Bulduk
3 March 1162

4. CRICKETING PARLANCE

The nautical world has given us countless words and expressions which are an integral part of our everyday language.

So, too, with the world of cricket.

Who wrote the following?

(a) 'For when his legs were smitten off
He fought upon his stumps.'

(b) 'Many a heart is aching if you could read them all.
Many the hopes that have vanished after the ball.'

(c) 'He that toucheth pitch shall be defiled therewith.'

(d) 'There St John mingles with my friendly bowl.'

(e) 'Am I my brother's keeper?'

(f) 'It's all a load of balls, matey.'

(g) 'I am the batsman and the bat.
I am the bowler and the ball,
The Umpire, the pavilion cat,
The roller, pitch and stumps and all.'

5. ODD MAN OUT

I well remember being in the presence of the Northampton-shire and England all-rounder, Robert Bailey, who was proudly proclaiming that he was the only famous man he knew to have had a shipping forecast area named after him.

I struck him sharply on the knuckles with my cake fork and barked:

'Wrong, sir.

'You have forgotten Fred Astaire.'

He hoisted his south cones and flounced off looking decidedly odd.

Who is the odd one out among the following?

(a) R.C. Robertson-Glasgow, Neville Cardus, Tony Lewis, Frances Edmonds, Denzil Bachelor, Martin Johnson, E.W. Swanton.

(b) Queen Victoria, Queen Salote of Tonga, Queen Wilhel-mina, Tony Lewis, King Zog, Princess Alice of Athlone, Princess Grace of Monaco.

(c) My friend, the Commodore, Frances Edmonds, Barbara Dixon, Eleanor Oldroyd, Elaine Page, Sarah Goatman, Sue Lawley, Her Majesty the Queen.

(d) Herbert Strudwick, George Duckworth, Wally Grout, Don Tallon, Rodney Marsh, George Dawkes, Len Maddocks, my friend, the Commodore, Godfrey Evans, Frank Mooney.

6. STOP PRESS

This is indeed 'The Golden Age' of cricket journalism.

The willow strikes the crimson rambler.

The groundsman's horse nods sleepily in his fudded stable.

The tea urn croons and gurgles its tannin lullabies.

The flannelled fools disport themselves on firm-bosomed sward.

And the gentlemen of the press sit in Olympian splendour in their box and we lesser mortals sit humbly at their feet scrabbling for morsels from the banquets of their mellifluous lubricity.

The beauty of their language moves us to tears.

Their tenderness, their generosity, their originality cause pimples to rill goose-like across our yielding flesh.

The following extracts were taken from a variety of newspapers on Friday 3 June 1994.

Find the writer.

Find the newspaper.

(a) 'De Freitas has made more comebacks than Frank Sinatra and Lazarus put together.'

(b) 'After more rejection slips than a pulp novelist Phil De Freitas returned to the England set-up yesterday . . .'

(c) 'For eight years he has been a mystery man with a stop–start international career in which he jokingly refers to himself as cricket's Frank Sinatra because of his endless comebacks.'

(d) 'The England paceman who has made more reappearances than an old James Bond film . . .'

(e) 'De Freitas' *My Life and Tantrums* would rival the Judy Garland story any day.'

(f) '. . . someone once remarked that Philip De Freitas had made more comebacks than Frank Sinatra.'

7. CRICKET GROUNDS

I was but three years of age when my father of late and loathsome memory first took me to a cricket ground.

He was attacked by stoats.

At an 'impressionable age' I saw Mr Raymond 'Madonna' Illingworth squirting Mr Bill Alley with TCP at Bramall Lane, Sheffield.

The Lady Wife was once impaled on a slip cradle during the entire luncheon adjournment, Somerset versus the New Sealand tourists, County Ground, Taunton.

Martin Donnelly scored 38.

Happy memories.

Happy happy memories.

The cricket grounds of England!

Names, the redolence of whose beauty and nobility expresses the very heart and soul of our blessed native land.

Which teams play or have played at the following grounds?

Baker Perkins Sports Ground
Snibston Colliery Ground
Winger Sports Ground
Sports Centre, Hammarskjold Road
Hoover Sports Ground
Allied Brewery Sports Ground
Mothercare Sports Centre, Keating New Town
Racecourse Ground, Hereford
Courtaulds Sports Ground
Decca Sports Ground
Westland Sports Ground
John Player and Sons Sports Ground
Lord's
Midland Bank Sports Ground
US Officers' Ground
Eno's Sports and Athletic Centre

8. LITERARY GIANTS

Cricket has long been a precious source of fascination and inspiration for writers from every corner of the globe.

Would Chekhov have achieved the sublime greatness of *The Cherry Orchard* had he not once witnessed three successive late cuts by Mr Winston Place?

What price the fame and reputation of Jane Austen had she not once been no-balled nineteen times in an innings by Mr Cec Pepper during the Cheltenham Festival?

Would Mr Tim Rice have scaled such heights had he not been suckled at the breast till the age of puberty by Mr Jonathan Agnew?

In this vein, what were the works of a cricketing nature written by the following great writers?

T.H. White
Graham Greene
Joseph Heller
John Wyndham
Flann O'Brien
Ernest Hemingway
Evelyn Waugh
William Shakespeare
H.E. Bates
Graham Greene
T.E. Lawrence
Captain W.J. Johns
Edna O'Brien
D.H. Lawrence
Gabriel Chevallier
Jean Rhys
Gustave Flaubert
Arthur Ransome
George Bernard Shaw
Richard Hughes
Noël Coward
John Lennon
Samuel Beckett
Christopher Isherwood
Paul Brickhill
Terence Rattigan

Evelyn Waugh
William Shakespeare
John Wain
James Jones
Joseph Conrad
H.G. Wells
J.B. Priestley
Thomas Mann
Peter Tinniswood

9. WHERE IS THY STING?

It comes to us all.
    Oh yes, my friends, so it does.
    You ask Victor Trumper.

Who died at the following places?

Cheadle, Cheshire
1 November 1902

Mottingham, Kent
23 October 1915

Witney Scrotum
21 December 1936

Tooting Bec
4 October 1962

Beverly Hills, California
20 December 1935

Witney Scrotum
21 December 1949

Branksome, Dorset
8 July 1973

Beauty Point, New South Wales
25 August 1968

Montreux, Switzerland
18 June 1958

Witney Scrotum
21 December 1995

At Sea, Læsø, Denmark
19 December 1930

THE ANSWERS

All right, all right.

I can hear the smart alecks even now rasping through the coarse-throated smoke of their cheap-jack, duty-free cheroots and sleeking their cheeks on the flanks of their ghastly mobile phones.

'He's wrong. Course he's wrong. He doesn't know what he's talking about. It's a load of bollocks. You ask Frances Edmonds. She knows everything there is to know about bollocks.'

And I can hear the congenital whingers sucking the caps on their leaking ballpoints and scuffling the buckles on their train spotters' surgical sandals.

'That's not fair. No one could possibly know that. I once saw Bill Frindall buying a packet of wholemeal crumpets in Tesco's so I should know what I'm talking about.'

And I can hear the grumpers and the grousers snuffling into their lager shandies and dousing their shirt tails with Dabitoff.

'I don't care anyway. It's a complete waste of time, this so-called quiz. Isn't it scandalous you can't buy decent jacket potatoes for love nor money these days?'

Well, listen to me, you spineless scum.

I don't care what you think.

These are the answers.

And they're all correct.

So get on with it and no bloody arguing.

Oh by the way – there is just one thing.

There's a deliberate mistake in the answers.

Just one.

I wonder if you can spot it.

I'm damned if I can.

1. FAMOUS FIRST LINES

(a) Ray Illingworth: *Yorkshire and Back*

(b) Frances Edmonds: *Another Bloody Tour*

(c) Len Hutton: *Cricket Is My Life*

(d) Bill Bowes: *Express Deliveries*

(e) Jack Hobbs: *The Fight for the Ashes*

(f) Wally Hammond: *Cricket Is My Destiny*

(g) Don Bradman: *Farewell to Cricket*

(h) Denis Compton: *End of an Innings*

(i) Doug Insole: *Cricket from the Middle*

(j) Marjorie Pollard: *Cricket for Women and Girls*
(A book much thumbed by Mr Chris Lewis of Nottinghamshire and England.)

2. MIDDLE NAMES

Conrad Hunte
Doug Insole
Alvin Kallicharran
Bill Johnston
Alan Kippax
Jim Laker
Vijay Manjrekar
Mike Procter
Don Shepherd of our beloved Glamorgan
Bobby Simpson
John Snow
Gary Sobers
Jeff Stollmeyer
Fred Titmus
Freddie Trueman – he's going to change it by deed poll
to Knowall
Clive Van Ryneveld
Ajit Wadekar
Clyde Walcott
Everton Weekes
Neil Adcock
Les Ames
Warwick Armstrong
Eddie Barlow
Don Bradman
Peter Burge
Bhagwat Chandrasekhar
Bill Edrich
W.G. Grace
Richard Hadlee

Vijay Hazare
Jack Hobbs
Charlie Elliott
(Nice chap, Charlie. The Lady Wife once informed me that she would like to suck his kneecaps.)

3. BIRTHPLACES

Norman Gifford
David Gower
Grannie Swanton, Mantovani and King Leopold of the Belgians
Pat Pocock
Ken Higgs
Jack Simmons – with a bag of chips in his mouth
The saintly Winston Place
Matthew Engel
Keith Fletcher
Derek Pringle
Sir Pelham Warner
Genghis Khan and Mr Raymond Illingworth

4. CRICKETING PARLANCE

(a) Richard Sheale: *Ballad of Chevy Chase*

(b) Charles K. Harris: *After the Ball*

(c) The Old Testament, Ecclesiasticus

   (I hope I've spelled it correctly)

(d) Alexander Pope: *Satires and Epistles of Horace Imitated* (rumoured to be the favourite reading of Mr Philip Tufnell)

(e) The Old Testament, Genesis

(f) Keith Fletcher: *Letters to a Friend from a Sojourn in The West Indies*

(g) Mr Raymond 'Madonna' Illingworth
(Or is it Andrew Lang Brahms?)

5. ODD MAN OUT:

(a) Tony Lewis – all the others are respected writers.

(b) King Zog – all the others bowled left-handed.

(c) Her Majesty the Queen – all the others like dressing in women's clothing.

(d) My friend, the Commodore – none of the others ever painted his toenails carmine.

6. STOP PRESS

(a) John Etheridge: *Sun*

(b) Mike Selvey: *Guardian*

(c) Chris Lander: *Daily Mirror*

(d) Mike Beale: *Daily Star*

(e) Michael Henderson: *The Times*

(f) Peter Deeley: *Daily Telegraph*

7. CRICKET GROUNDS

Northamptonshire

Leicestershire
Gloucestershire
Essex – and wouldn't you know it?
Glamorgan – our much beloved county beyond The Dyke
Derbyshire
No one – the potties don't work in the umpires' urinals
Worcestershire
Warwickshire
Surrey
Somerset
Nottinghamshire
I've looked it up in all my Wisdens and I'm damned if
I can find the answer
Kent
Hampshire
The Bronchial Wanderers, The Snufflers and Mervyn Bragg

8. LITERARY GIANTS

The Once and Future Collis King
F.G. Mann in Havana
Catch 22 Not Out
The Krikken Wakes
At Swim Two Dickie Birds
To Have and Have Knott
Put Out More Faggs
Twelfth Man
The Darling Lloyd Budds of Peter May
The Third Man
The Seven Pullars of Wisdens
Gimblett Mops Up
Casualties of Pearce

Sons and Govers
The Affairs of Flavell
Tiger Smith Is Better Looking
Madame Avery
Pridgeon Post
Ames and the Man
In Hazare
Hay Hever
Return To Fender
Waiting For Goddard
Arthur Morris Changes Trains
The Lamb Busters
Separate Abels
Vile Bedis
Vijay Merchant of Venice
Murray On Down
Zaheer to Eternity
Stollmeyer's Folly
The History of Mr Polly Umrigar
Dangerous Horner
Todd in Venedig
A Touch of Wayne Daniel

9. WHERE IS THY STING?

Johnny Briggs – what a lovely man he was
W.G. Grace
An unknown leg spinner
Patsy Hendren
Sir Aubrey Smith
Another unknown leg spinner
Wilfred Rhodes

Stan McCabe
Douglas Jardine – rum place to snuff it, isn't it?
A leg spinner with protruding ears
J.W.H.T. Douglas – why does that bring a warm glow to my
heart?

I've spotted the deliberate mistake.
  Genghis Khan was born in Pudsey.

8